Volume One

Sadlier Math

Catherine D. LeTourneau

Allan E. Bellman, Ph.D.

Jill A. Perry, Ph.D.

Sadlier School

The Publisher of *Progress in Mathematics*

Program Reviewers

The publisher wishes to thank for their comments and suggestions the following teachers and administrators, who read portions of the series prior to publication.

Cover Series Design: Silver Linings Studios

Photo Credits

Cover: Alamy Stock Photo/age fotostock: *bottom*; iStockphoto.com/ThomasTakacs: *top*.

Interior: Associated Press/David Duprey: 239, 240. Dreamstime.com/Olga Kostenko: *2 background, 52 background, 110 background, 144 background, 194 background, 240 background*. Fotolia.com/IvicaNS: 51, 52. Getty Images/Keren Su: 193, 194. Shutterstock.com/Zurijeta: 109, 110; Sean Pavone: 143, 144; Billion Photos: 1, 2. United States coin images from the United States Mint.

Ilustrators

Bob Holt, Scott Borroughs, Sarah Beise, Nathan Jarvis, Jose Ramos, Joseph Taylor. Shutterstock.com/Agor2012, incredible_movements, miniaria, whanwhan.ai, Zmiter.

 is a registered trademark of William H. Sadlier, Inc.

Printed in the United States of America.
ISBN: 978-1-4217-8982-8
5 6 7 8 9 10 SHNW 26 25 24 23 22

For additional online resources, go to SadlierConnect.com.

Welcome to Sadlier Math

Dear Second Grader,

Do you know why math is important? Well, we all use math every day. We use it when we:

- measure an object
- read a map
- shop
- solve a puzzle
- build something
- and much more!

Throughout this book are special signs and symbols. When you see them, be sure to stop and look.

Objective This is what you will be studying in the lesson.

Math Words Look at these words. They are important words for the lesson.

Problem Solving Get ready to apply math in real-world contexts.

Write About It This is a question or topic for you to write about.

PRACTICE These are exercises for you to show what you know.

MORE PRACTICE These are exercises for you to build more understanding.

HOMEWORK These are exercises for you to do at home.

We wrote this book just for you!

The Authors

Hi. We are your new math friends. When you see us, pay attention. We have a lot to say!

CONTENTS

Chapter 1 Addition Within 20

Chapter 2 Subtraction Within 20

Chapter 3 Place Value to 100

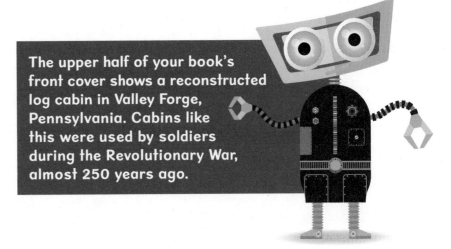

The upper half of your book's front cover shows a reconstructed log cabin in Valley Forge, Pennsylvania. Cabins like this were used by soldiers during the Revolutionary War, almost 250 years ago.

Chapter 4 Addition: Two-Digit Numbers

Chapter 5 Subtraction: Two-Digit Numbers

Chapter 6 Measurement

Chapter 7 Place Value to 1000

The log cabins at Valley Forge were about 16 feet long by 14 feet wide. Each cabin could house up to 12 soldiers.

Chapter 8 Addition: Three-Digit Numbers

The lower half of the front cover shows the Hemisfèric (in the foreground) and the Palau de les Arts (in the background). These buildings are part of the City of Arts and Sciences in Valencia, Spain.

Chapter 9 Subtraction: Three-Digit Numbers

Chapter 10 Foundations for Multiplication

The Palau de les Arts is a performing arts center used mainly for operas. With a height of 75 meters, it is the tallest opera house in the world.

Chapter 11 Data and Graphical Displays

Chapter 12 Money and Time

Chapter 13 Geometry

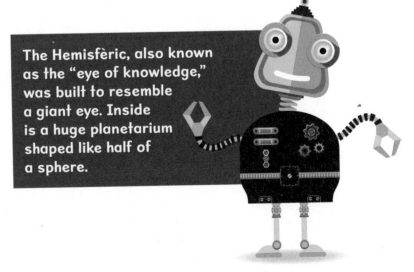

The Hemisfèric, also known as the "eye of knowledge," was built to resemble a giant eye. Inside is a huge planetarium shaped like half of a sphere.

Chapter 14 Equal Shares

What do you do when faced with a math problem you don't know how to solve?

Read Read the problem.
Study the facts.
Know what the
question asks.

Plan What will you do
to solve the problem?

Solve Work your plan.
Write your answer.
Make sure to label
your answer.

To be a super
problem solver,
follow these steps.

Check Does your answer
make sense?
Work the problem
in a different way.
Did you get the
same answer?

Read the next pages with your teacher and your family.
You will find strategies and math practices to help you
solve problems.

Write and solve an equation.

Read this problem.

Lucy finds 2 🐚. Her sister finds I 🐚.
Her friend finds 5 🐚.
How many 🐚 do they find in all?

Solve the problem using an
addition equation.

$$2 + 1 + 5 = ?$$

**Ask yourself some key questions
to help you solve the problem.**

- How can I use an equation
to show the problem?

- How can I use what is
known to write an
equation?

- What steps should I use to
solve the equation?

- Can I use models to solve
the problem?

Use Logical Reasoning.

Read this problem.

Spencer spins the pointer and lands on a number. The number is greater than 20 and less than 30. It has 5 ones. What is Spencer's number?

You can use reasoning to answer the question. Look at each clue.

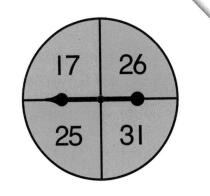

Ask yourself some key questions to help you answer the problem.

- What words in the problem are clues?

- What is my plan for solving the problem?

- How does each clue help me find the answer?

- How can I explain my reasoning using words?

- How can I explain my reasoning using words?

Use a Model

Read this problem.

Mike has 8 .
He gives some ⊙ to Ali.
He has 5 ⊙ left over.
How many ⊙ did Mike give to Ali?

You can draw circles in a bar model to solve the problem.

$$8 - ? = 5$$

Total number

⊙ ⊙ ⊙ ⊙ ⊙ ⊙ ⊙ ⊙

Number Mike gives to Ali	Number left over
?	⊙ ⊙ ⊙ ⊙ ⊙

Ask yourself some key questions to help you answer the problem.

- What do I know?

- What am I trying to find out?

- How can a model help me solve the problem?

- How does the model show the information in the problem?

- How can I explain the parts of the model?

- How can I use the model to show that my answer is correct?

Work Backward

Read this problem.

Bob buys an apple for 35¢. He has 10¢ left. How much money did Bob have to start?

You can work backward to solve the problem.

Bob spent 35¢.

He has 10¢ left.

Add to find the total.

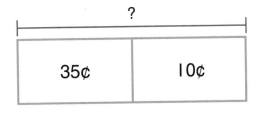

$$35¢ + 10¢ = 45¢$$

Ask yourself some key questions to help you answer the problem.

- What do I know?

- How do I know that I need to work backward to solve the problem?

- How can I use a diagram to help me work backward?

- Can I use an equation to solve the problem?

- How can I check my answer?

Draw a Picture.

Read this problem.

Cesar buys 3 boxes of markers.
Each box has 5 markers in it.
How many markers does Cesar buy in all?

You can draw a picture to show the total number of markers.

The number of rows shows the number of boxes. The number of columns shows the number of markers in each box.

Cesar: 3 boxes of 5

□ □ □ □ □

□ □ □ □ □

□ □ □ □ □

Ask yourself some key questions to help you answer the problem.

- How can drawing a picture help me understand the problem?

- What are some ways to show the parts of the problem?

- What other pictures can I draw to show the problem?

- Can I explain my picture to a classmate or my teacher?

- How can the picture help me solve the problem?

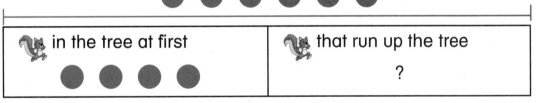

MP 1: Make sense of problems.

Look at this problem.

There are 4 🐿 in a tree. More 🐿 run up the tree. Now there are 6 🐿.

How many more 🐿 run up the tree?

Write an addition equation with ? for the number you do not know. This is the unknown addend.

$$4 + ? = 6$$

This bar model shows what you do know.

Total number of 🐿

Think
What do I know?

● ● ● ● ● ●

🐿 in the tree at first ● ● ● ●	🐿 that run up the tree ?

You need 2 more counters to make 6. $4 + 2 = 6$.

➤ So, 2 more 🐿 run up the tree.

Ask yourself some key questions to help you answer the problem.

- How can I describe the problem in my own words?

- What is my plan to solve the problem?

- Can I draw a picture to help me understand the problem better?

- How can I show that my answer makes sense?

MP 2: Use reasoning.

Read this problem.

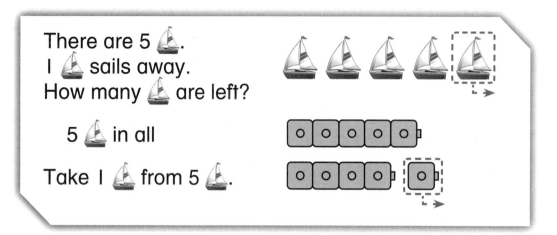

There are 5 ⛵.
1 ⛵ sails away.
How many ⛵ are left?

5 ⛵ in all

Take 1 ⛵ from 5 ⛵.

Ask yourself some key questions to help you solve the problem.

- How is this problem like problems I solved before?

- What is my plan to solve this problem?

- How can I use the picture to help me understand the problem better?

- Should I add or subtract to solve the problem?

- How can I explain my answer using words and numbers?

MP 3: Explain your reasoning.

Read this problem.

Maddy picks 4 .

Sophia picks 7 .

Who picks more? Who picks fewer?

You can choose addition
or subtraction to find the answer.

Sophia picks 4 plus

how many more to equal 7?

$4 + ? = 7$

**Ask yourself some key questions
to help you solve the problem.**

- How do I know what the problem is asking me to find?

- How does a drawing help me explain my reasoning?

- Why did I choose this strategy to solve the problem?

- Why does my strategy work?

- How can I show that my answer is correct?

MP 4: Model with mathematics.

Read this problem.

Levi has some ● with his dinner. How many ● does Levi have?

You can make groups of tens and ones to help you count large numbers.

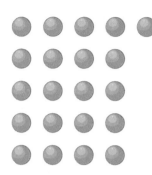

Ask yourself some key questions to help you answer the question.

- How can I use a model to show the problem?

- What will the model show me about the problem?

- What key words do I need to understand?

- Can a picture help me understand the problem?

- How can I use words or math symbols to solve the problem?

- What will the answer look like in the model?

MP 5: Use the right tools.

Read this problem.

Summer has some .

Georgia has 5 .

They have 9 in all.

How many does Summer have?

Summer has _____ .

Total Number is 9.

_____ + 5 = 9

Ask yourself some key questions to help you answer the problem.

- What do I know?

- What am I trying to find out?

- Why is it helpful to use models to show the problem?

- Can I use pencil and paper to draw a picture?

- How can I use models to show the problem?

- How can I show that my answer makes sense?

MP 6: Be precise.

Read this problem.

Lauren counts some 🌸 in a field.
How many 🌸 does Lauren count?

Find how many tens
and how many ones.

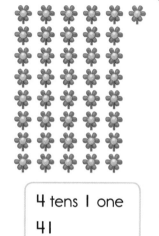

tens	ones
	▫

4 tens 1 one

41

forty-one

Lauren counts 4 tens and 1 one.
The number of 🌸 is 41, or forty-one.

Ask yourself some key questions to help you answer the problem.

- What do I know?

- What is the problem asking me to do?

- Can I draw or mark a picture to help me understand the problem better?

- How can I use math words to explain the problem?

- Does my answer make sense for the problem?

- How can I show that my answer is correct?

MP 7: Look for a pattern.

Read this problem.

Erik colors two patterns in his 120 chart.
What patterns did Erik find?

> I more or I less

> 10 more or 10 less

1	2	3	4	5	6	7	8	9	10
11	12	13	14	15	16	17	18	19	20
21	22	23	24	25	26	27	28	29	30
31	32	33	34	35	36	37	38	39	40
41	42	43	44	45	46	47	48	49	50
51	52	53	54	55	56	57	58	59	60
61	62	63	64	65	66	67	68	69	70
71	72	73	74	75	76	77	78	79	80
81	82	83	84	85	86	87	88	89	90
91	92	93	94	95	96	97	98	99	100
101	102	103	104	105	106	107	108	109	110
111	112	113	114	115	116	117	118	119	120

Ask yourself some key questions to help you answer the problem.

- What patterns do I see?
- Is there a pattern rule I can use?
- What would the pattern look like if the numbers in the chart went up to 200?

- How can the patterns I see help me solve other problems?
- How would I explain my work to a classmate or my teacher?

MP 8: Generalize.

Read this problem.

Kylee scored 84 points bowling.
Lucy scored 10 less than Kylee.
How many points did Lucy score bowling?

You can use mental math to
find 10 less. Start at 84.

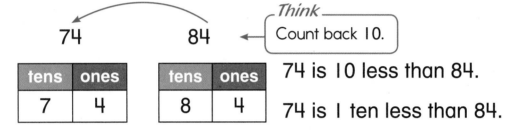

Think —
Count back 10.

tens	ones
7	4

tens	ones
8	4

74 is 10 less than 84.

74 is 1 ten less than 84.

⟩ Lucy scored 74 total points bowling.

Ask yourself some key questions to help you solve the problem.

- Is this problem like other problems I have solved?

- What is the important informaiton in this problem?

- How can circling and underlining information help me solve the problem?

- Is there any information given that is not needed?

- What is my plan to solve the problem?

- How might this strategy work in other situations?

Addition Within 20

Scientists study atoms. Atoms are too small to see. But they make up everything around us!

Building Blocks

♦ The centers of atoms are made of protons and neutrons. Different kinds of atoms have different numbers of each. An oxygen atom has 8 protons and 8 neutrons.

Study and Classify

♦ Atomic mass is the total number of protons and neutrons an atom has. If you know the atomic mass, then you know what kind of atom it is!

♦ How can you find the atomic mass of an oxygen atom?

Dear Family,

In this chapter, we will learn about adding numbers through 20.

Here are some Key Math Words for this chapter:

addend

sum

related addition facts

doubles

near doubles

make 10

Associative Property

unknown addend

pattern rule

You can use the glossary to find the definition of each word and help your child make flash cards to study each day we work on the lessons for this chapter.

During this chapter we also will be making STEAM (Science, Technology, Engineering, the Arts, and Mathematics) connections about atoms. Read the opening to the chapter together and discuss the **Building Blocks** and **Study and Classify** statements.

Keep Your Skills Sharp

Here is a **Keep Your Skills Sharp** activity to do at home to prepare for this chapter.

Show two groups that each contain from 1 to 10 small objects. Discuss how many objects there are in all and ways to find the total.

Name_____

Addition Concepts

There are 3 ladybugs on a leaf.
Then 5 more ladybugs join them.
How many ladybugs are there in all?

Objective
- Use addition to find the unknown sum or addend in word problems.

Math Words
add
equation
plus sign (+)
equals =

To find how many in all, add 5 to 3 in an equation.
An equation is a number sentence with an = sign.

$3 + 5 = ?$

$3 + 5 = 8$, so there are 8 ladybugs in all.

PRACTICE

Add. You may use red and blue cubes to help.

1. $7 + 6 =$ _____ ◻◻◻◻◻◻◻ + ◻◻◻◻◻◻

2. $9 + 8 =$ _____	3. $14 + 0 =$ _____	4. _____ $= 5 + 9$
5. $5 +$ _____ $= 11$	6. _____ $+ 8 = 16$	7. $20 = 15 +$ _____

8. 9 $+3$	9. 5 $+4$	10. 8 $+0$	11. 9 $+6$
12. 4 $+7$	13. 17 $+\ 3$	14. 2 $+8$	15. 12 $+\ 4$

Problem Solving

16. There are 8 cats sitting near a tree.
    Then 4 more cats come to sit.
    How many cats in all are sitting near the tree?

    There are _____ cats in all sitting near the tree.

17. There are 7 boys playing ball.
    Then some more boys join the game.
    There are 12 boys in all playing ball.
    How many boys join the game?

    _____ boys join the game.

18. Some pencils were in a box. Sue put 6
    more pencils in. The picture shows
    how many pencils are in the box now.
    How many pencils were in the box at
    the start?

    There were _____ pencils in the box at the start.

Write About It

19. Abby had 10 red apples. Then she picked some
    green apples. Now she has 17 apples in all.
    How many green apples does Abby have?
    Write an equation. Then solve the problem.
    Explain how you found your answer.

    _____

    _____

    _____

Addition Concepts

There are 3 ladybugs on a leaf.
Then 5 more ladybugs join them.
How many ladybugs are there in all?

To find how many in all, add 5 to 3 in an equation.
An equation is a number sentence with an = sign.

$3 + 5 = ?$

$3 + 5 = 8$, so there are 8 ladybugs in all.

MORE PRACTICE

Add. You can use red and blue cubes to help.

1. 7 + ____ = 10	2. ____ + 8 = 13	3. 7 + ____ = 19

4. 1 7 + 0	5. 6 + 7	6. 7 + 4	7. 4 + 6

8. There are 6 frogs on a log.
   Then 6 more frogs join them.
   How many frogs in all are on the log?

   $6 + 6 = ?$

   There are ____ frogs on the log.

Add. You can use red and blue cubes to help.

1. $3 + \_\_\_ = 16$	2. $\_\_\_ + 0 = 15$	3. $10 + \_\_\_ = 18$

4. $\begin{array}{r} 1\,1 \\ +\ 9 \\ \hline \end{array}$	5. $\begin{array}{r} 1\,7 \\ +\ 1 \\ \hline \end{array}$	6. $\begin{array}{r} 1\,2 \\ +\ 7 \\ \hline \end{array}$	7. $\begin{array}{r} 0 \\ +1\,6 \\ \hline \end{array}$

8. There are 6 white cars in a parking lot. Then some blue cars park in the lot. There are 10 cars in all. How many blue cars are there?

There are ___ blue cars.

Problem Solving

9. 12 muffins can fit on a plate. Logan puts 5 muffins on the plate. How many more muffins can Logan fit on the plate?

$5 + ? = 12$

Logan can fit ___ more muffins on the plate.

Write About It

10. Carla has 7 pairs of blue socks and 6 pairs of white socks. Emma has 4 pairs of red socks and 10 pairs of pink socks. Who has more pairs of socks? Explain your thinking.

_____

_____

_____

Name _____

Put Together

Objective
- Use addition to solve word problems about putting objects together.

Math Words
addend
sum

Jack has 6 red cubes and 4 blue cubes.
How many cubes does he have in all?

Add to find how many in all. 6 + 4 = ?

$$6 + 4 = 10$$

addend   addend   sum

Numbers that you add are called addends.
The sum is the number in all.

▷ Jack has 10 cubes in all.

Annie has 12 cubes. 7 of the cubes are red.
The rest of the cubes are blue.

How many blue cubes does Annie have?

red cubes		blue cubes		total cubes
7	+	?	=	12
7	+	5	=	12

▷ Annie has 5 blue cubes.

PRACTICE

Add. You may use red and blue cubes to help.

1. 5 + 8 = ____

2. 5 + ____ = 9

3. 6 + 9 = ____

4. 10 = ____ + 3

Add.

5. _____ = 2 + 10

6. 12 + 5 = _____

7. _____ + 3 = 19

8. 6
   + 3
   ___

9. 9
   + 7
   ___

10.   8
    + ☐
    ___
      14

11.   ☐
    + 2
    ___
      10

12.   ☐
    + 10
    ____
     20

Problem Solving

13. Louise picks 5 red flowers and 7 yellow flowers. How many flowers does she pick in all?

Louise picks _____ flowers in all.

14. Jack has 11 marbles in his pocket. 4 of the marbles are green. The rest are blue. Write an equation to show this. Use ? for how many blue marbles.

_____

_Write About It

15. Julia has 13 fish in her fish tank. She has 6 goldfish and the rest are clown fish. How many clown fish does she have? Explain how you found your answer.

_____

_____

_____

Name _____

Put Together

Jack has 6 red cubes and 4 blue cubes.
How many cubes does he have in all?

Add to find how many in all. $6 + 4 = ?$

6	+	4	=	10
addend		addend		sum

Numbers that you add are called addends.

The sum is the number in all.

▷ Jack has 10 cubes in all.

MORE PRACTICE

Complete the addition. You can use red and blue cubes to help.

1. $7 + \underline{\quad} = 10$	2. $10 + 9 = \underline{\quad}$	3. $15 = \underline{\quad} + 5$

4. $\begin{array}{r}\square \\ +\ 4 \\ \hline 9\end{array}$	5. $\begin{array}{r}11 \\ +\ 3 \\ \hline \end{array}$	6. $\begin{array}{r}9 \\ +\ \square \\ \hline 16\end{array}$	7. $\begin{array}{r}\square \\ +\ 12 \\ \hline 12\end{array}$	8. $\begin{array}{r}\square \\ +\ 7 \\ \hline 19\end{array}$

9. Judy sees 8 robins and 8 cardinals.
   How many birds does Judy see in all?

   $8 + \underline{\quad} = \underline{\quad}$

   Judy sees ___ birds in all.

Complete the equation.

1. ___ + 2 = 11

2. 9 + 8 = ___

3. 12 = ___ + 4

4.
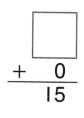
```
  □
+ 0
───
 15
```

5.
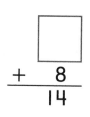
```
  □
+ 8
───
 14
```

6.
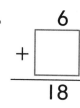
```
   6
+  □
───
 18
```

7.
```
  □
+ 11
───
 14
```

8.
```
  □
+ 3
───
 16
```

9. Emma has 7 green balloons and 6 yellow balloons.
How many balloons does Emma have in all?
Write an equation and solve it.

___ + ___ = ___

Emma has ___ balloons in all.

Problem Solving

10. There are 15 animals on a farm.
There are 9 cows and the rest are horses.
How many horses are on the farm?

There are ___ horses on the farm.

Write About It

11. There are 6 bananas and some apples in a bowl.
There are 12 pieces of fruit in all in the bowl. How
many apples are in the bowl? Explain your answer.

_____

_____

_____

Name _____

Related Addition Facts

Objective
- Add two numbers in any order.

Math Words
addend
order
sum
related addition
  facts

Marco connects 3 red cubes to 8 blue cubes. What two facts show how many cubes he has in all?

The facts have the same addends.
Only the order is different.

$$3 + 8 = 11$$
$$8 + 3 = 11$$

You can add numbers in any order.
The sum is the same.

▷ 3 + 8 = 11 and 8 + 3 = 11 are related addition facts.

They show that Marco has 11 cubes.

PRACTICE

Write related addition facts for the model.

1.

____ + ____ = ____ and ____ + ____ = ____

2.

____ + ____ = ____ and ____ + ____ = ____

Find the sum. Write the related addition fact.

3. 9 + 7 = ____

____ + ____ = ____

4. 8 + 5 = ____

____ + ____ = ____

5.
```
   9
 + 3
```
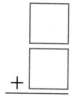

+ ☐

6.
```
   5
 + 6
```
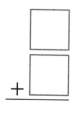

+ ☐

7.
```
  1 3
 +  5
```
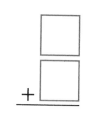

+ ☐

Write the number that makes the equation true.

8. 18 + 0 = ____ + 18

9. ____ + 2 = 2 + 14

Problem Solving

10. Louis has 13 toy cars and 7 toy trucks. Carlos has the same total number of cars and trucks. He has 7 toy cars. How many toy trucks does Carlos have?

Carlos has ____ toy trucks.

Write About It

11. Pat says that 5 + 9 = 14 and 11 + 3 = 14 are related addition facts because both sums are 14. Explain why Pat is not correct.

_____

_____

_____

12 ▪ twelve

LESSON 1-3

Name _____

Count On to Add

When one addend is 1, 2, or 3, start with the greater addend. Count on to find the sum.

$$3 + 5 = 8$$

| 5 is greater than 3. Start at 5. | Count on 3. 6, 7, 8 |

MORE PRACTICE

Circle the greater addend. Find it on the diagram. Count on to find the sum.

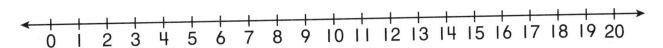

1. $2 + 6 =$ ___ | 2. $3 + 10 =$ ___ | 3. $1 + 5 =$ ___

4. Put an **X** in the box for the number that makes the equation true.

	1	2	3
$5 + ? = 7$	☐	☐	☐
$? + 5 = 8$	☐	☐	☐
$11 = 10 + ?$	☐	☐	☐

Circle the greater addend. Find it on the diagram.
Count on to find the sum.

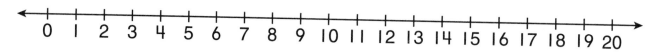

1. 5 + 1 = ____	2. 3 + 12 = ____	3. 2 + 11 = ____
4. 13 + 1 = ____	5. ____ = 2 + 3	6. ____ = 14 + 2

7. $\begin{array}{r} 2 \\ + 5 \\ \hline \end{array}$	8. $\begin{array}{r} 8 \\ + 3 \\ \hline \end{array}$	9. $\begin{array}{r} 1 \\ + 9 \\ \hline \end{array}$	10. $\begin{array}{r} 2 \\ + 7 \\ \hline \end{array}$

Problem Solving

11. Kim picks 3 apples. Then she picks 12 more apples.
How many apples does Kim pick in all? Write an
equation to show your work.

_____

_____

Write About It

12. There are 9 turtles and 11 fish swimming in a pond.
One more turtle jumps in to swim. How many
turtles are swimming now? Explain how you found
the answer.

_____

_____

_____

Name _____

Doubles and Near Doubles

Kavi has a group of 7 tennis balls and a group of 8 tennis balls. How many tennis balls does Kavi have in all?

Math Words
doubles
near doubles
doubles + 1
doubles − 1
one more
one less

A doubles fact has two addends that are the same.
To find 7 + 8, use a near doubles fact.

Doubles + 1	**Doubles − 1**

Think
7 + 7 = 14

Think
8 + 8 = 16

Since 8 is one more than 7, 7 + 8 is one more than 7 + 7.

14 + 1 = 15

So, 7 + 8 = 15.

Since 7 is one less than 8, 7 + 8 is one less than 8 + 8.

16 − 1 = 15

So, 7 + 8 = 15.

▷ Kavi has 15 tennis balls.

PRACTICE

Complete the facts.

Doubles	Doubles + 1	Doubles − 1
1. 4 + ___ = ___	4 + ___ = ___	4 + ___ = ___
2. ___ + 8 = ___	___ + 8 = ___	___ + 8 = ___

Complete the facts.

3. $10 + 10 = $ ____	**4.** ____ $= 2 + 3$	**5.** $7 + $ ____ $= 13$
6. $4 + $ ____ $= 7$	**7.** $6 + 5 = $ ____	**8.** ____ $= 9 + 8$

Problem Solving

9. There are 17 students in a class. The number of girls is one more than the number of boys. How many girls are in the class? How many boys are in the class? Explain using a doubles fact.

_____

_____

_____

_____

Write About It

10. Hector and Mark use near doubles to find the sum $6 + 7$. Hector uses the doubles fact $7 + 7 = 14$. Can Mark use a different doubles fact and get the same sum? Explain your answer.

_____

_____

_____

Name _____

Doubles and Near Doubles

You can use doubles facts to find the sums of near doubles.

Doubles + 1	**Doubles − 1**
Think $7 + 8 \leftarrow \boxed{7 + 7 = 14}$	Think $7 + 8 \leftarrow \boxed{8 + 8 = 16}$
Since 8 is one more than 7, 7 + 8 is one more than 7 + 7.	Since 7 is one less than 8, 7 + 8 is one less than 8 + 8.
$14 + 1 = 15$	$16 - 1 = 15$
So, $7 + 8 = 15$.	So, $7 + 8 = 15$.

MORE PRACTICE

Complete the facts.

Doubles	Doubles + 1	Doubles − 1
1. $3 + \underline{\quad} = \underline{\quad}$	$3 + \underline{\quad} = \underline{\quad}$	$3 + \underline{\quad} = \underline{\quad}$
2. $\underline{\quad} + 6 = \underline{\quad}$	$\underline{\quad} + 6 = \underline{\quad}$	$\underline{\quad} + 6 = \underline{\quad}$

Add.

3. $5 + 6 = \underline{\quad}$	4. $\underline{\quad} = 7 + 8$	5. $3 + 4 = \underline{\quad}$
6. $4 + 5 = \underline{\quad}$	7. $\underline{\quad} = 9 + 8$	8. $6 + 7 = \underline{\quad}$

Complete the facts.

Doubles	Doubles + 1	Doubles − 1
1. 5 + ___ = ___	5 + ___ = ___	5 + ___ = ___
2. ___ + 8 = ___	___ + 8 = ___	___ + 8 = ___

Add.

3. 2 + 3 = ___	4. 6 + 7 = ___	5. 5 + 4 = ___
6. 6 + 5 = ___	7. 9 + 8 = ___	8. 4 + 3 = ___

Problem Solving

9. Carl and his sister are putting together puzzles. His sister's puzzle has 8 pieces. Carl's puzzle has one fewer than double the number of pieces in his sister's puzzle. How many pieces are in Carl's puzzle? Explain.

_____

_____

Write About It

10. There are 11 fish. There is one fewer orange fish than yellow fish. How many of each color fish are there? Explain.

_____

_____

_____

Name _____

Make 10 to Add

Objective
• Make 10 to find the sum of two numbers.

Math Words
make 10
sum
ten-frame

Ana has 8 tomatoes. She buys 5 more tomatoes. How many tomatoes does Ana have in all?

When one addend is close to 10, you can make 10 to find the sum. Fill a ten-frame to make 10.

$8 + 5 = ?$ Model the addends with counters. Use 8 red counters and 5 blue counters.

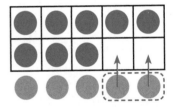

$8 + 2 + 3 = ?$ Move 2 counters from the 5 to the 8 to make 10.

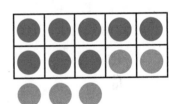

$10 + 3 = 13$ 10 + 3 is the same as 8 + 5, so $8 + 5 = 13$.

Ana has 13 tomatoes.

PRACTICE

Add by making 10. Use the ten-frame to help.

1. $9 + \quad 7 \quad = ?$

   $9 + \underline{\quad} + \underline{\quad} = ?$

   $\underline{\quad} + \underline{\quad} = \underline{\quad}$

   $9 + 7 = \underline{\quad}$

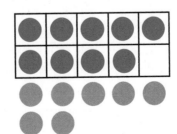

Draw counters to make 10. Then add.

2. $4 + 9 = ?$

___ + ___ + 9 = ___

$4 + 9 =$ ___

Add.

3. $9 + 3 =$ ___

4. ___ $= 6 + 9$

5. $8 + 6 =$ ___

Problem Solving

6. Leona uses 5 cups of oats to make muffins. She uses 9 cups of oats to make granola bars. How many cups of oats does Leona use in all? Explain how to make 10 to solve.

_____

_____

Write About It

7. Jessica made this model with a ten-frame to find $3 + 8$. Explain how she can use the model to find the sum.

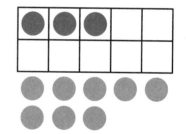

_____

_____

_____

_____

Name _____

Make 10 to Add

When one addend is close to 10, you can make 10 to find the sum.

$8 + 5 = ?$

$8 + 2 + 3 = ?$

$10 + 3 = 13$

So, $8 + 5 = 13$.

$8 + 5 = ?$

Think

$8 + ? = 10.$

Since $8 + 2 = 10$, break 5 into $2 + 3$.

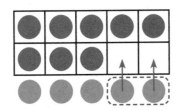

So, $8 + 5 = 13$.

MORE PRACTICE

Add by making 10. Use the ten-frame to help.

1. $9 \quad + 8 \qquad = ?$

   $9 \quad + \underline{\quad} + \underline{\quad} = ?$

   $\underline{\quad} + \underline{\quad} \qquad = \underline{\quad}$

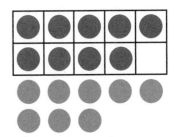

2. $4 + 8 = ?$

   $\underline{\quad} + \underline{\quad} + 8 = \underline{\quad}$

   $4 + 8 = \underline{\quad}$

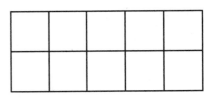

Add.

3. $9 + 9 = \underline{\quad}$

4. $\underline{\quad} = 8 + 6$

5. $7 + 8 = \underline{\quad}$

Draw counters to make 10. Then complete the addition and find the sum.

1. $9 + 5 = ?$

   $9 + \underline{} + \underline{} = \underline{}$

   $9 + 5 = \underline{}$

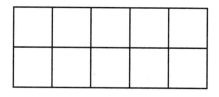

2. $6 + 6 = ?$

   $6 + \underline{} + \underline{} = \underline{}$

   $6 + 6 = \underline{}$

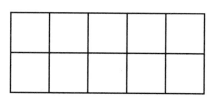

Problem Solving

3. Cora has 14 roses. 8 of them are red. The rest are yellow. How many yellow roses does Cora have?

   Cora has \underline{} yellow roses.

Write About It

4. Ivan has a stack of 7 coins and a stack of 8 coins. How many coins does Ivan have in all? Explain how you can make 10 to find out.

_____

_____

_____

_____

Name _____

Three Addends

Objective
■ Use mental strategies to add three numbers.

Math Words
strategies
count on
doubles
make 10

Alex collects 2 green leaves, 8 yellow leaves, and 2 red leaves. How many leaves does he collect in all?

Add $2 + 8 + 2$ to find the total number of leaves.

You have learned different strategies for adding 2 numbers. Use the strategies and group the addends in different ways to make the addition easier.

Count on	Doubles	Make 10
Start with 8. Count on 2. $8 \longrightarrow 9, 10$ Count on 2 more from 10. $10 \longrightarrow 11, \mathbf{12}$	First use the doubles fact $2 + 2 = 4$. Then add 4 to 8. $8 + 4 = \mathbf{12}$	First add 2 and 8 to make 10. Then add 2 to 10. $10 + 2 = \mathbf{12}$

Alex collects 12 leaves.

PRACTICE

Add. Circle the addends you added first.

1. $5 + 1 + 5 =$ _____

2. $9 + 3 + 7 =$ _____

3. $4 + 9 + 1 =$ _____

4. $2 + 13 + 5 =$ _____

Add. Circle the addends you added first.

5.
```
   4
   7
 + 6
```

6.
```
   8
   8
 + 2
```

7.
```
   2
   9
 + 4
```

8.
```
   4
   9
 + 4
```

Add.

9.
```
   9
   0
 + 1
```

10.
```
   5
   2
 + 4
```

11.
```
   3
   6
 + 3
```

12.
```
   5
   1
 + 9
```

Problem Solving

13. Noah has 4 stickers and Mario has 6 stickers.
Raja has the same number of stickers as Mario.
How many stickers do they have in all?
Write your strategy and solve.

_____

_____

Write About It

14. What different strategy could you use to solve the
problem about Noah, Mario, Raja, and their
stickers? Would it change the answer? Explain.

_____

_____

_____

Name _____

Three Addends

Look at the different ways you can add 2 + 8 + 2.

Count on	Doubles	Make 10
Start with 8. Count on 2. 8 ⟶ 9, 10 Count on 2 more from 10. 10 ⟶ 11, **12**	First use the doubles fact 2 + 2 = 4. Then add 4 to 8. 8 + 4 = **12**	First add 2 and 8 to make 10. Then add 2 to 10. 10 + 2 = **12**

MORE PRACTICE

Add. Circle the addends you added first.

1. 5 + 6 + 5 = ____

2. 2 + 12 + 3 = ____

3. 4 + 1 + 7 = ____

4. 2 + 4 + 6 = ____

5.
$$\begin{array}{r} 7 \\ 3 \\ + 8 \\ \hline \end{array}$$

6.
$$\begin{array}{r} 4 \\ 7 \\ + 4 \\ \hline \end{array}$$

7.
$$\begin{array}{r} 6 \\ 2 \\ + 8 \\ \hline \end{array}$$

8.
$$\begin{array}{r} 5 \\ 6 \\ + 2 \\ \hline \end{array}$$

9.
$$\begin{array}{r} 6 \\ 4 \\ + 9 \\ \hline \end{array}$$

10.
$$\begin{array}{r} 2 \\ 7 \\ + 5 \\ \hline \end{array}$$

11.
$$\begin{array}{r} 3 \\ 5 \\ + 7 \\ \hline \end{array}$$

12.
$$\begin{array}{r} 10 \\ 6 \\ + 4 \\ \hline \end{array}$$

Add.

1. $6 + 6 + 1 = \underline{\quad}$	2. $3 + 5 + 6 = \underline{\quad}$
3. $9 + 6 + 1 = \underline{\quad}$	4. $7 + 3 + 7 = \underline{\quad}$

5. $\begin{array}{r} 1 \\ 7 \\ +\ 3 \\ \hline \end{array}$	6. $\begin{array}{r} 5 \\ 5 \\ +\ 9 \\ \hline \end{array}$	7. $\begin{array}{r} 7 \\ 1 \\ +\ 9 \\ \hline \end{array}$	8. $\begin{array}{r} 3 \\ 3 \\ +\ 6 \\ \hline \end{array}$

Problem Solving

9. Cameron buys 3 toys at a yard sale. He uses the Make 10 strategy to find the total amount of money he spends. Circle 3 toys he could have bought. Write how much Cameron spent on those toys.

 6¢  2¢   7¢  3¢  4¢

Cameron spent ___ ¢ on the toys.

Write About It

10. Write an addition equation with 3 addends that could be added using the Count On, Doubles, or Make 10 strategy. Explain how each strategy would work.

_____

_____

_____

Name _____

Problem Solving Read〉Plan〉Solve〉Check
Use the Four-Step Process

A class counts 4 owls, 6 hawks, and 7 crows in a forest. How many birds in all does the class count?

Add 4 + 6 + 7 to find the total number of birds.

You can group the numbers in different ways. The Associative Property says that the sum will be the same.

Look at the numbers being added and make a plan. Which strategy can you use?

Make 10	Doubles + 1
The addends 4 and 6 can be added first to make 10.	The addends 6 and 7 are a near double.
$(4 + 6) + 7 = ?$	Use Doubles + 1.
$10 + 7 = 17$	$6 + 6 = 12$, so $6 + 7 = 13$
$4 + 6 + 7 = \mathbf{17}$	$4 + 13 = \mathbf{17}$

Both strategies give the same sum.

▷ The class counts a total of 17 birds.

Read each problem. Make a plan. Then solve.

1. Brandon is filling water balloons. He fills 3 blue, 5 red, and 7 yellow balloons. How many balloons does he fill in all?

   Brandon fills _____ balloons in all.

2. Ana and Suri each score 4 points. Cara scores 6 points. How many points do they score in all?

   They score _____ points in all.

3. Anaya and Gwen each take 2 cards and add the numbers of dots on the cards. Both girls have the same total number of dots. How many dots are on Gwen's other card?

   Anaya's Cards   **Gwen's Cards**

   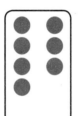   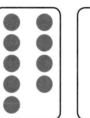

   There are _____ dots on Gwen's other card.

Write About It

4. Jamal has 7 baseball cards and 9 football cards. He also has some basketball cards. He uses the doubles strategy to find the total number of cards. How many basketball cards could Jamal have? Explain how you know.

   _____

   _____

   _____

Problem Solving
Use the Four-Step Process

A pet shop sold 2 mice, 8 fish, and 2 birds.
How many animals did the pet shop sell?

Make a plan. Choose a strategy.
Remember, you can group numbers in different ways
and get the same sum.

Count on. Then add again.	Make 10. Then add again.	Use doubles. Then add again.
$2 + (8) + (2)$ $8 \longrightarrow 9, 10$ $10 + 2 = 12$	$2 + (8 + 2)$ $10 + 2 = 12$	$(2) + 8 + (2)$ $4 + 8 = 12$

The pet shop sold 12 pets.

MORE PRACTICE

Read each problem. Make a plan. Then solve.

1. Maya has 5 red pencils. She has the same number
   of green pencils as red pencils. She also has 9 blue
   pencils. How many pencils does Maya have in all?

   Maya has _____ pencils.

2. Troy and Dylan play a game. Troy scores 8 points.
   Dylan scores 9 points. How many points do Troy
   and Dylan score in all?

   Troy and Dylan score _____ points.

Read each problem. Make a plan. Then solve.

3. Blake sees 7 frogs in a pond. Shen sees 2 more frogs than Blake. How many frogs do Blake and Shen see in all?

   Blake and Shen see _____ frogs.

4. Ethan buys 3 bookmarks. He uses the Make 10 strategy to find how much he spends. Circle the bookmarks Ethan could have bought. Write how much he spends on those bookmarks.

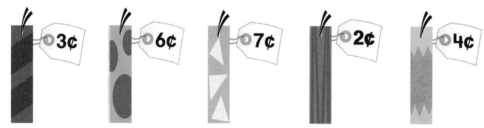

   Ethan spends _____ ¢.

5. Grace has 9 stamps. Jane has 2 fewer stamps than Grace. They want to find how many stamps they have in all.

   Grace and Jane use different strategies to solve this problem.

Grace	Jane
$9 + 2 = 11$ $11 + 9 = 20$	$9 - 2 = 7$ $7 + 9 = 16$
We have 20 *stamps* in all.	We have 16 *stamps* in all.

   Who has the correct answer? _____

   Describe the mistake the other child made.

   _____

   _____

Name _____

Read each problem. Make a plan. Then solve.

1. Sarah is having fun at the beach.
   She finds 6 seashells. Then she finds 5 more.
   How many seashells does Sarah find in all?

   Sarah finds ____ seashells in all.

2. There are 15 fish in the tank. Seven of the fish are large.
   The rest are small. How many small fish are in the tank?

   There are ____ small fish in the tank.

3. Chase and Taylor are setting up chairs for a play.
   Chase sets up rows of 4, 3, and 7 chairs. Taylor sets
   up 3 more chairs in all than Chase sets up.
   How many chairs do they each set up?

   Chase sets up ____ chairs.

   Taylor sets up ____ chairs.

4. Sofia reads 8 books over summer break. Her brother
   reads 3 fewer books than she reads. How many
   books do Sofia and her brother read in all?

   They read ____ books in all.

5. Michael and Jack have the same total number of blocks.
   Michael has 6 small blocks and 8 large blocks. Jack has
   8 small blocks. How many large blocks does Jack have?

   Jack has ____ large blocks.

Oscar and Logan see 7 red, 5 blue, and 2 purple marbles in a box. They each choose a different strategy to find the total number of marbles in the box.

Oscar says he will use the Count On strategy.

Logan says he will use the Make 10 strategy.

Use this information to answer Exercises 6–10.

6. Will both strategies work? _____

7. Whose strategy will work? _____

8. Use the correct strategy to solve the problem.

_____

_____

_____

9. How many marbles are in the box?

There are ____ marbles in the box.

10. Describe why the other strategy will not work.

_____

_____

_____

_____

Name _____

Solve for Unknown Addends

Ana has 15 stickers in all. Some stickers are stars and 7 are hearts. How many stickers are stars?

You can use a bar model and an equation to find the number of star stickers.

Objective
▪ Use drawings and equations to find an unknown addend.

Math Words

bar model
equation
unknown addend
doubles
doubles + 1

Draw a bar model.

Write an equation with an unknown addend.

$? + 7 = 15$

whole

15

?	7
part	part

Use a strategy you know to find the unknown addend.

Doubles: $7 + 7 = 14$

Doubles + 1: $8 + 7 = 15$

The unknown addend is 8.

▷ Ana has 8 star stickers.

PRACTICE

Draw a bar model and write an equation to solve the problem.

sum

1. Nevyn wants to put 12 animal patches on his backpack. He has 9 animal patches. How many more patches does he need?

$? + \underline{9} = \underline{12}$

Nevyn needs __3__ more animal patches.

Find the unknown addend.

2. $5 + \underline{5} = 10$

3. $\underline{7} + 7 = 14$

4. $17 = 9 + \underline{8}$

5. $\underline{} + 13 = 15$

6. $9 = \underline{} + 3$

7. $9 + \underline{} = 19$

Problem Solving

8. Write a word problem for the bar model. Then write an equation and solve the problem. Describe your strategy.

10	
?	5

_____

_____

_____

_____

Write About It

9. Jonas says the unknown addends in these equations are the same.

$$? + 3 = 12 \qquad 12 = 3 + ?$$

How can Jonas know this without solving either equation?

_____

_____

_____

_____

Name _____

Patterns in Addition

Objective
■ Complete and explain patterns found in addition sentences.

Math Words
pattern rule
addend
sum

Macy uses cubes to show a pattern in addition equations. What is the next equation in the pattern?

To find what comes next, look for a pattern rule.

$1 + 5 = 6$

$2 + 4 = 6$

$3 + 3 = 6$

Think

The first addend goes up by 1.

The second addend goes down by 1.

The sum stays the same.

A rule for the pattern is the first addend goes up by 1, the second addend goes down by 1 and the sum stays the same.

The next addition equation in the pattern is

$4 + 2 = 6$

PRACTICE

**Use the model to complete the addition pattern.
Write the pattern rule.**

1. $3 + 4 = 7$

   $3 + 5 = 8$

   $3 + 6 = 9$

   ___ + ___ = ___

   _____

   _____

Complete the addition patterns.

2. $9 + 3 =$ ____

    $8 + 4 =$ ____

    $7 + 5 =$ ____

    ___ + ___ = ___

3. $6 + 5 =$ ____

    $7 + 5 =$ ____

    $8 + 5 =$ ___

    ___ + ___ = ___

Problem Solving

4. Marco is making a pattern with addition equations. He uses 13 cubes to show $6 + 7$, 14 cubes to show $7 + 7$, and 15 cubes to show $8 + 7$. How many cubes will Marco use to show the next addition equation? Explain how you know.

_____

_____

_____

Write About It

5. Describe a pattern rule shown by these addition equations. Explain how both the addends and the sums change.

$$\begin{array}{r} 1 \\ +\ 2 \\ \hline 3 \end{array} \qquad \begin{array}{r} 2 \\ +\ 3 \\ \hline 5 \end{array} \qquad \begin{array}{r} 3 \\ +\ 4 \\ \hline 7 \end{array} \qquad \begin{array}{r} 4 \\ +\ 5 \\ \hline 9 \end{array}$$

_____

_____

Name _____

Patterns in Addition

You can find patterns in addition equations. Look at how the addends change. What is the next equation in the pattern?

⬜⬜⬜⬜⬜⬜   1 + 5 = 6

⬜⬜⬜⬜⬜⬜   2 + 4 = 6

⬜⬜⬜⬜⬜⬜   3 + 3 = 6

The first addends go up by 1. The second addends go down by 1. The sums stay the same.

➤ The next addition equation is 4 + 2 = 6.

MORE PRACTICE

Use the model to complete the addition pattern.

1. △△△△◯◯◯◯◯   4 + 5 = 9

   △△△△△◯◯◯◯   ___ + ___ = 9

   △△△△△△◯◯◯   ___ + ___ = 9

   △△△△△△△◯◯   ___ + ___ = ___

2.    3 + 7 = 10

   ___ + ___ = 11

   ___ + ___ = 12

   ___ + ___ = ___

Fill in the missing sums. Then write the next two addition facts in the pattern.

1.
$$\begin{array}{r} 5 \\ +\ 9 \\ \hline \end{array} \qquad \begin{array}{r} 6 \\ +\ 8 \\ \hline \end{array} \qquad \begin{array}{r} 7 \\ +\ 7 \\ \hline \end{array}$$

  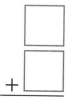

2.
$$\begin{array}{r} 8 \\ +\ 9 \\ \hline \end{array} \qquad \begin{array}{r} 7 \\ +\ 9 \\ \hline \end{array} \qquad \begin{array}{r} 6 \\ +\ 9 \\ \hline \end{array}$$

Problem Solving

3. Each second-grade class at a school has the same number of students. One class has 8 boys and 11 girls. Another class has 9 boys and 10 girls. There are 10 boys in Rolf's second-grade class. How many girls are there in his class?

There are _____ girls in Rolf's class.

Write About It

4. Elani wrote this pattern of addition facts.

   $3 + 3 =$ _____ $4 + 4 =$ _____ $5 + 5 =$ _____

   Elani says the sums will increase by 1 since both addends increase by 1. Is she correct? Explain.

   _____

   _____

Name _____

Add. Write the sum.

1. $5 + 2 = $ ___

2. $3 + 7 = $ ___

3. $10 + 9 = $ ___

Add. Circle the correct answer.

4.
$$\begin{array}{r} 3 \\ + 9 \\ \hline \end{array}$$

A. 6

B. 12

C. 13

5.
$$\begin{array}{r} 14 \\ + 6 \\ \hline \end{array}$$

A. 9

B. 19

C. 20

6.
$$\begin{array}{r} 2 \\ + 6 \\ \hline \end{array}$$

A. 4

B. 8

C. 18

Which number makes the equation true?

7. $5 + 13 = 13 + ?$

A. 5

B. 13

C. 18

8. $7 + ? = 8 + 7$

A. 1

B. 8

C. 15

Count on to find the sum.

9. $3 + 9 = $ ___

10. $12 + 1 = $ ___

11. ___ $= 2 + 18$

Complete the doubles or near-doubles facts.

12. $6 + 6 = $ ___

13. $10 + 10 = $ ___

14. $7 + $ ___ $= 13$

Draw counters to make 10. Then complete the addition.

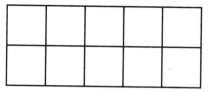

15. $8 + 6 = ?$

$8 + 6 = 10 +$ _____

$8 + 6 =$ _____

Which equations can also be used to find the sum?

16. $3 + 6 + 7 = ?$

    A. $9 + 7 = 16$

    B. $13 + 6 = 19$

    C. $10 + 6 = 16$

17. $8 + 8 + 2 = ?$

    A. $16 + 4 = 20$

    B. $16 + 2 = 18$

    C. $8 + 10 = 18$

Find the unknown addend.

18. _____ $+ 8 = 16$

19. $11 = 6 +$ _____

20. $4 +$ _____ $= 17$

Complete the addition patterns.

21. $8 + 6 =$ _____

$9 + 5 =$ _____

$10 + 4 =$ _____

_____ $+$ _____ $=$ _____

22. $4 + 7 =$ _____

$5 + 7 =$ _____

$6 + 7 =$ _____

_____ $+$ _____ $=$ _____

23. Alison draws 18 shapes. She draws 2 squares and 8 circles. The rest of the shapes are triangles. How many triangles does Alison draw?

Alison draws _____ triangles.

Name _____

The table shows the numbers of protons and neutrons in the centers of some atoms.

1. Add the number of protons and number of neutrons to find the atomic mass of each atom.

Atomic Masses			
Atom	Number of Protons	Number of Neutrons	Atomic Mass
Hydrogen	1	0	$1 + 0 =$ _____
Boron	5	6	$5 + 6 =$ _____
Carbon	6	6	$6 + 6 =$ _____
Oxygen	8	8	$8 + 8 =$ _____

2. A neon atom has an atomic mass of 20. It has 10 protons. How many neutrons does a neon atom have? Write an equation you could use to solve the problem.

_____

3. Write an unknown addend question about one of the types of atoms in the table. Then solve it.

_____

_____

_____

_____

_____

Determine the best answer for each problem.

1. Add. $8 + 9 = ?$

   A. 16
   B. 17
   C. 18

2. Add. $13 + 2 = ?$

   A. 11
   B. 14
   C. 15

3. Add. $\begin{array}{r} 7 \\ + 7 \\ \hline \end{array}$

   A. 14
   B. 15
   C. 16

4. Write the missing number in the equation.

   $6 + \underline{} = 18$

5. Complete the addition pattern.

   $11 + 4 = \underline{}$

   $10 + 5 = \underline{}$

   $9 + 6 = \underline{}$

   $\underline{} + 7 = \underline{}$

6. Add. $\begin{array}{r} 7 \\ 8 \\ + 2 \\ \hline \end{array}$

   A. 15
   B. 17
   C. 18

7. Grace picks 6 peaches. Then she picks 7 more peaches. How many peaches does Grace pick in all?

   _____ peaches

8. In different rounds of a game, Mac scores 2 points, 7 points, and 7 points. Which equations show Mac's total points?

   A. $9 + 7 = 16$
   B. $14 + 2 = 16$
   C. $10 + 7 = 17$

Subtraction Within 20

A video is a record. It can show a fun day. It can show a pretty butterfly. You can take and watch videos on a camera or phone. You can take and watch videos on a tablet or computer.

Editing Videos

♦ Sometimes a video is too long. It can be edited. Editing is like cutting out part of the video. The edited video is called a clip.

How It Works

♦ Use a computer app to edit a video. Move the line where you want to cut. Cut it to take that part out.

♦ How is editing a video like subtracting?

Dear Family,

In this chapter, we will be learning about subtracting numbers through 20.

Here are some key Math Words for this chapter:

subtract

take apart

compare

difference

fact family

related subtraction facts

related addition and subtraction facts

subtraction equation

You can use the glossary to find the definition of each word and help your child make flash cards to study them every day.

During this chapter we also will be making STEAM (Science, Technology, Engineering, the Arts, and Mathematics) connections about using technology to edit videos. Read the opening to the chapter together and discuss the **Editing Videos** and **How It Works** statements.

Keep Your Skills Sharp

Here is an activity to do at home to prepare for this chapter.

Have your child count up to 20 small objects and place them in a paper bag. Take out 3 objects and ask your child to guess how many objects are in the bag now. Then let your child pour out the objects and count them. Repeat the activity.

Name _____

Subtraction Concepts

You can take away some from a group.

You can subtract to find how many are left.

Liam has 6 cubes.
He gives 2 cubes to Paul.
How many cubes does Liam have left?

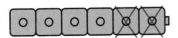

$6 - 2 = 4$

➤ Liam has 4 cubes left.

You can subtract to find one part of a whole.

Joan has 9 cubes.
3 are red.
The rest are blue.
How many cubes are blue?

$$\begin{array}{r} 9 \quad \text{whole} \\ -\ 3 \quad \text{part} \\ \hline 6 \quad \text{part} \end{array}$$

➤ 6 cubes are blue.

PRACTICE

Subtract. You can use cubes to help.

1. $8 - 5 =$ _____

2. $12 - 5 =$ _____

3. $9 - 6 =$ _____

4. _____ $= 14 - 4$

5. _____ $= 15 - 6$

Find the unknown number to complete the subtraction.

6. $11 - \underline{\hspace{1cm}} = 5$ **7.** $\underline{\hspace{1cm}} - 8 = 8$ **8.** $20 - 15 = \underline{\hspace{1cm}}$

9. $\underline{\hspace{1cm}} - 6 = 4$ **10.** $13 - \underline{\hspace{1cm}} = 6$ **11.** $11 - 8 = \underline{\hspace{1cm}}$

Subtract.

12.
$$\begin{array}{r} 9 \\ -3 \\ \hline \end{array}$$

13.
$$\begin{array}{r} 17 \\ -10 \\ \hline \end{array}$$

14.
$$\begin{array}{r} 8 \\ -0 \\ \hline \end{array}$$

15.
$$\begin{array}{r} 12 \\ -3 \\ \hline \end{array}$$

Problem Solving

16. Ethan has 18 coins. He puts 12 coins in his pocket and the rest in his bank. How many coins does Ethan put in his bank? Write and solve a subtraction equation to match the problem.

_____

Write About It

17. Kati has 14 markers. She gives 5 markers to her sister and 3 to her brother. Kati says she has 7 markers left. Is Kati correct? Explain how you know.

_____

_____

_____

_____

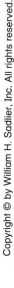

Name _____

Take Apart

Dylan has 10 balloons. He gives 3 to his
brother and keeps the rest for himself.
How many balloons does Dylan keep?

Objective
▪ Take apart groups
to subtract.

Math Word
take apart

You can subtract to take apart a group and
make two smaller groups.

whole group	smaller group	smaller group
10	− 3	= 7

▷ Dylan keeps 7 balloons.

PRACTICE

Complete the subtraction. You can use cubes to help.

1. 8 − 2 = ____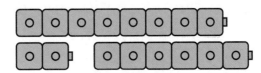

2. 10 − 6 = ____	3. 12 − 7 = ____	4. ____ = 15 − 6
5. 14 − ____ = 8	6. ____ − 9 = 10	7. 16 − 8 = ____

Subtract.

8.   16
    − 6

9.   15
    − 12

10.   19
    − 8

11.   10
    − 6

Problem Solving

12. There are 9 children playing in the park. Then 2 of the children leave. The rest continue to play. How many children are playing in the park now?

    There are _____ children playing in the park.

13. Andrew has 15 crackers. He has 3 rice crackers and 5 cheese crackers. The rest are animal crackers. How many animal crackers does Andrew have?

    Andrew has _____ animal crackers.

Write About It

14. Write a subtraction problem to match this picture. Then answer the problem.

_____

_____

_____

Subtract to Compare

Maxine has 8 marbles. Deena has 3 marbles.

How many more marbles does Maxine have than Deena?

You need to compare the number of marbles Maxine has to the number of marbles Deena has.

Maxine's marbles:

Deena's marbles:

You can subtract Deena's marbles to compare.

$8 - 3 = 5$

Maxine has 5 more marbles than Deena.

PRACTICE

Subtract. You can use cubes to help.

1. Jared has 12 toy trains. Clark has 7 toy trains.
   How many fewer toy trains does Clark have than Jared?

   ⬜⬜⬜⬜⬜⬜⬜⬜⬜⬜⬜⬜
   ⬜⬜⬜⬜⬜⬜⬜

   _____ – _____ = _____

   Clark has _____ fewer toy trains than Jared.

Subtract to compare.

2. Kayla picks 15 yellow flowers and 3 pink flowers. How many fewer pink flowers does Kayla pick than yellow flowers?

Kayla picks _____ fewer pink flowers.

Problem Solving

3. Maria sees 6 red birds and 4 blue birds in the garden. Then she sees 5 butterflies. How many more birds than butterflies does Maria see? Draw a picture to show the problem.

Maria sees _____ more birds than butterflies.

Write About It

4. In a class, 10 students say they have a cat as a pet and 7 say they have a hamster as a pet. Write and solve a compare question about the students' pets.

_____

_____

Subtract to Compare

Kim has 8 basketballs and 3 soccer balls. How many more basketballs than soccer balls does Kim have?

You can subtract to compare.

8 − 3 = 5

Kim has 5 more basketballs than soccer balls.

MORE PRACTICE

Subtract. You can use cubes to help.

1. Jackson got 9 cards on Monday. He got 3 cards on Tuesday. How many more cards did Jackson get on Monday than on Tuesday?

   Jackson got _____ more cards on Monday than on Tuesday.

2. Skylar rode her bike 10 miles. Alexa rode her bike 6 miles. How many fewer miles did Alexa ride than Skylar?

   Skylar:

   Alexa:

   Alexa rode _____ fewer miles than Skylar.

Subtract. You can use cubes to help.

1. There are 12 turtles and 8 frogs in a pond.
   How many more turtles than frogs are in the pond?

There are ____ more turtles than frogs.

2. Pedro has 14 red balloons and 5 blue balloons.
   How many fewer blue balloons than red balloons
   does he have?

   Pedro has ____ fewer blue balloons than red balloons.

Problem Solving

3. Santos has 14 crayons. He has 3 more crayons
   than Karl. Karl has 4 more crayons than Jamal.
   How many crayons does Jamal have?

   Jamal has ____ crayons.

Write About It

4.

   Write a question comparing the shapes. Then write and
   solve a subtraction equation to answer the question.

   _____

   _____

Count On to Subtract

Jen rides her bike 13 blocks. Darla rides her bike 7 blocks. How many more blocks does Jen ride than Darla?

You can subtract to find how many more or how many fewer.

Count on from the lesser number to the greater number to find the difference.

Think of the difference as a missing addend.

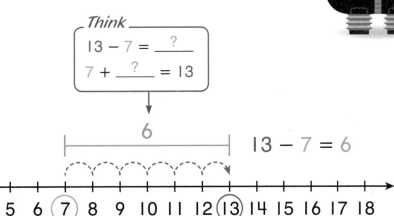

Think

$13 - 7 = \underline{\quad?\quad}$

$7 + \underline{\quad?\quad} = 13$

6

$13 - 7 = 6$

0 1 2 3 4 5 6 ⑦ 8 9 10 11 12 ⑬ 14 15 16 17 18

Jen rides 6 more blocks than Darla.

PRACTICE

Circle the lesser number on the line diagram. Count on to find the difference.

1. $12 - 8 = \underline{\quad}$

Think

$8 + \underline{\quad?\quad} = 12$

0 1 2 3 4 5 6 7 8 9 10 11 12 13 14 15 16 17 18

Count on to find the difference. You can use the line diagram to help you.

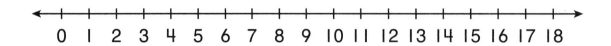

2. $10 - 9 =$ _____

3. $14 - 8 =$ _____

4. $11 - 2 =$ _____

5. $13 - 6 =$ _____

Problem Solving

6. Elisa buys 3 goldfish at the pet store. Fran buys 12 goldfish. How many fewer goldfish does Elisa buy? Explain how you found your answer.

_____

_____

_____

Write About It

7. Explain how to think about the unknown addend in $2 + ? = 10$ as the difference in a subtraction.

_____

_____

_____

Count On to Subtract

Subtract to find how many more or how many fewer.
You can count on from the lesser number to the
greater number to find the difference.

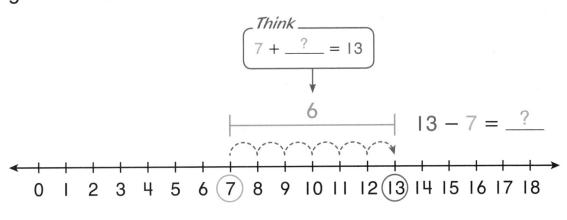

Think

7 + ___?___ = 13

6

13 − 7 = __?__

0 1 2 3 4 5 6 ⑦ 8 9 10 11 12 ⑬ 14 15 16 17 18

13 − 7 = 6

MORE PRACTICE

**Rewrite each subtraction problem as an addition
problem with an unknown addend.**

1. 13 − 5 = ?

   ___ + ? = ___

2. 12 − 7 = ?

   ___ + ? = ___

**Count on to find the difference. You can use the
line diagram to help you.**

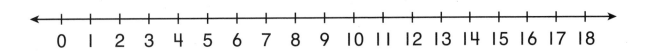

0 1 2 3 4 5 6 7 8 9 10 11 12 13 14 15 16 17 18

3. 10 − 7 = ___

4. 13 − 8 = ___

Count on to find the difference. You can use the line diagram to help you.

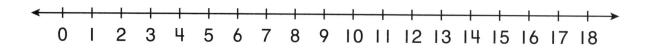

1. $10 - 4 =$ _____

2. $11 - 7 =$ _____

3. $12 - 3 =$ _____

4. $13 - 4 =$ _____

Problem Solving

5. A plate has 15 muffins on it. There are 6 berry muffins. The rest are raisin muffins. Write and solve an equation to show the number of raisin muffins.

   _____ – _____ = _____

   There are _____ raisin muffins.

Write About It

6. Rosa's kitten weighed 3 pounds when he was 3 months old. Now he weighs 9 pounds. How many pounds has the kitten gained since he was 3 months old? Explain how you found your answer.

   _____

   _____

   _____

   _____

Name _____

Related Subtraction Facts

Objective
• Write two related subtraction facts.

Math Word
related subtraction facts

Iris has 12 cubes that are either red or yellow. Three of the cubes are one color. The rest are the other color. How many yellow cubes could Iris have?

Use models to show two related subtraction facts.

The 3 cubes could be red:	The 3 cubes could be yellow:
12 − 3 = 9	12 − 9 = 3

Related facts use the same numbers.

➤ Iris could have either 9 or 3 yellow cubes.

PRACTICE

Subtract. Write the related subtraction fact.

1.

$11 - 5 = $ _____

_____ − _____ = _____

2.

$10 - 7 = $ _____

_____ − _____ = _____

3.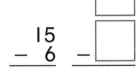

$\begin{array}{r} 15 \\ -\ 6 \end{array}$ − ☐

4.

$\begin{array}{r} 9 \\ -\ 7 \end{array}$ − ☐

5.

$\begin{array}{r} 12 \\ -\ 4 \end{array}$ − ☐

Match the related subtraction facts.

6. $7 - 5 = 2$ $7 - 1 = 6$

   $7 - 6 = 1$ $13 - 9 = 4$

   $13 - 5 = 8$ $7 - 2 = 5$

   $13 - 4 = 9$ $13 - 8 = 5$

Problem Solving

7. Pablo has 10 dinner rolls. He puts 4 rolls on one plate and the rest on a second plate. He carries one plate to the table. How many rolls could be on that plate? Write two related subtraction facts to explain your answer.

   _____

   _____

   _____

Write About It

8. Are $9 - 8 = 1$ and $8 - 1 = 9$ related subtraction facts? Explain how you know.

   _____

   _____

   _____

   _____

Relate Addition and Subtraction

Objective
- Write related addition and subtraction facts.

Math Word
related addition and subtraction facts

Kim joined 7 red paper clips to 3 blue paper clips to make a chain. Then she took off the 3 blue paper clips from the chain. Write two equations to show what Kim did.

Draw two models and write two equations.

10

10

$7 + 3 = 10$

$10 - 3 = 7$

The number added and the number taken away are the same.

$7 + 3 = 10$ and $10 - 3 = 7$ use the same numbers, so they are related addition and subtraction facts. They show what Kim did.

PRACTICE

Read the story. Write an addition equation and a subtraction equation to show what happens.

1. 7 birds sit in a tree.
   4 birds join them.
   Then the 4 birds leave.

   ___ + ___ = ___

   ___ − ___ = ___

2. 14 lions are at a watering hole. 6 lions leave. Then 6 other lions come.

   ___ − ___ = ___

   ___ + ___ = ___

Complete each related addition or subtraction fact.

3. $4 + 8 =$ _____

___ $- 8 =$ _____

4. $15 - 8 =$ _____

___ $+ 8 =$ _____

5. $7 + 4 =$ _____

___ $- 4 =$ _____

6. $8 + 5 =$ _____

___ $- 5 =$ _____

7. $15 - 6 =$ _____

___ $+ 6 =$ _____

8. $3 + 9 =$ _____

___ $- 9 =$ _____

Problem Solving

9. Bob had 14 pennies in his pocket. Then he took 5 pennies out. Bob later put some pennies back in his pocket. Now, Bob has 14 pennies in his pocket again. How many pennies did Bob put back in his pocket? Use related addition and subtraction facts to explain your answer.

_____

_____

_____

Write About It

10. Tyler subtracts $16 - 9$ and gets 8. How would Tyler know if he is correct? Use a related addition fact to explain how Tyler could check his answer.

_____

_____

_____

_____

Name_____

Relate Addition and Subtraction

In related addition and subtraction facts the same numbers are used.

$$7 + 3 = 10 \qquad 10 - 3 = 7$$

The number added and the number taken away are the same.

MORE PRACTICE

Match the related addition and subtraction facts.

1. $8 + 3 = 11$ $12 - 4 = 8$

   $9 + 2 = 11$ $11 - 3 = 8$

   $8 + 4 = 12$ $11 - 2 = 9$

   $9 + 3 = 12$ $12 - 3 = 9$

Read the story. Write an addition equation and a subtraction equation to show what happens.

2. Jamie finds 8 seashells.
   Then she finds 7 more seashells.
   She gives 7 shells to her little brother.

____ + ____ = ____

____ − ____ = ____

Read the story. Write an addition equation and a subtraction equation to show what happens.

1. A group of 6 owls are resting. Then 5 owls join them. Now 5 owls fly away.

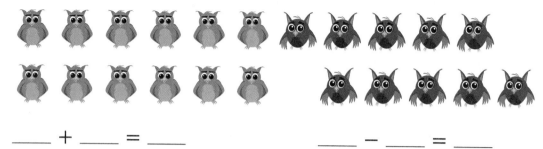

____ + ____ = ____   ____ − ____ = ____

Problem Solving

2. There were 6 children at a park when 7 more children arrived. Then some children left and there were 6 children at the park again. How many children left the park? Write related addition and subtraction facts and solve the problem.

____ + ____ = ____   ____ − ____ = ____

____ children left the park.

Write About It

3. Neveah had 10 books. Her brother borrowed 2 books. After her brother returned some books, Neveah had 10 books again. How many books did Neveah's brother return? Use related addition and subtraction facts to explain your answer.

_____

_____

_____

Name _____

Fact Families

A fact family is a set of all related facts for a group of numbers.

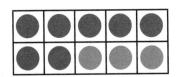

Here is the fact family for 4, 7, and 11.

$4 + 7 = 11$

$11 - 7 = 4$

$7 + 4 = 11$

$11 - 4 = 7$

PRACTICE

Complete each fact family.

1.

   $9 + 6 = $ ____

   ____ − ____ = ____

   ____ + ____ = ____

   ____ − ____ = ____

2.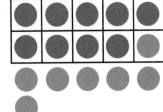

   ____ + ____ = ____

   ____ − ____ = ____

   ____ + ____ = ____

   ____ − ____ = ____

3.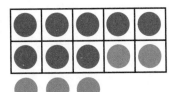

   ____ + ____ = ____   ____ − ____ = ____

   ____ + ____ = ____   ____ − ____ = ____

Complete each fact family.

4.

___ + ___ = ___   ___ + ___ = ___

___ − ___ = ___   ___ − ___ = ___

5.

☐   ☐   ☐   ☐
☐   ☐   ☐   ☐
+   −   +   −

Problem Solving

6. The numbers 9 and 5 can be used to make two different fact families. Write the missing number to show each fact family.

   Fact family 1:   9, 5, ___

   Fact family 2:   9, 5, ___

Write About It

7. Hector wants to write the fact family for 7, 7, and 14. He can only think of two facts. Is Hector missing facts? Explain why or why not and write the fact family.

   _____

   _____

   _____

   _____

Name _____

Subtract.

1. $10 - 5 =$ ___	2. $15 - 9 =$ ___	3. ___ $= 8 - 6$
4. $7 - 4 =$ ___	5. $18 - 9 =$ ___	6. ___ $= 12 - 3$

7. $\begin{array}{r} 9 \\ -7 \\ \hline \end{array}$	8. $\begin{array}{r} 12 \\ -\ 5 \\ \hline \end{array}$	9. $\begin{array}{r} 11 \\ -\ 4 \\ \hline \end{array}$	10. $\begin{array}{r} 16 \\ -\ 8 \\ \hline \end{array}$

Count on to find the difference. You can use the line diagram to help you.

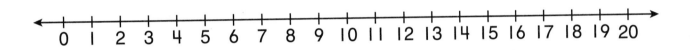

11. $10 - 9 =$ ___	12. $13 - 6 =$ ___	13. $14 - 8 =$ ___

Subtract. Write the related subtraction fact.

14. $8 - 7 =$ ___	15. $16 - 7 =$ ___	16. $12 - 8 =$ ___
___ $-$ ___ $=$ ___	___ $-$ ___ $=$ ___	___ $-$ ___ $=$ ___

17. 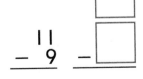 $\begin{array}{r} 11 \\ -\ 9 \\ \hline \end{array}$ $-\ \square$	18. $\begin{array}{r} 9 \\ -\ 4 \\ \hline \end{array}$ $-\ \square$	19. $\begin{array}{r} 15 \\ -\ 7 \\ \hline \end{array}$ $-\ \square$

Which is the related subtraction fact for the addition fact?

20. $5 + 8 = 13$

   A. $8 - 5 = 3$
   B. $13 - 8 = 5$
   C. $13 - 7 = 6$

21. $8 + 2 = 10$

   A. $8 - 2 = 6$
   B. $10 - 1 = 9$
   C. $10 - 2 = 8$

Complete each fact family.

22.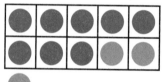

   ___ + ___ = ___

   ___ – ___ = ___

   ___ + ___ = ___

   ___ – ___ = ___

23.

   ___ + ___ = ___

   ___ – ___ = ___

   ___ + ___ = ___

   ___ – ___ = ___

Solve.

24. There are 9 squirrels in a park. Then 3 leave. How many squirrels are in the park now?

   There are ___ squirrels in the park now.

25. Isaiah ran 9 laps yesterday. He ran 13 laps today. How many more laps did Isaiah run today than yesterday?

   Isaiah ran ___ more laps today than yesterday.

Name _____

Think Addition to Subtract

Objective
- Use addition facts to subtract.

Math Word
related addition fact

Isabella is bowling. There are 10 pins. She knocks 6 down. How many pins are still standing?

Subtract to find how many pins are still standing.

You can think of a related addition fact to help you subtract.

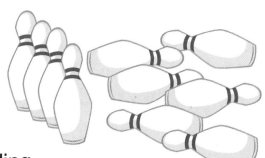

Think _____
$$10 - 6 = ?$$
$$4 + 6 = 10$$
So, $10 - 6 = 4$.

> There are 4 pins still standing.

PRACTICE

Subtract. Complete a related addition fact.

1. $11 - 4 = ?$

   ____ $+ 4 = 11$

   So, $11 - 4 =$ ____.

2. $13 - 8 = ?$

   ____ $+ 8 = 13$

   So, $13 - 8 =$ ____.

3. $15 - 6 = ?$

   ____ $+ 6 = 15$

   So, $15 - 6 =$ ____.

4. $12 - 6 = ?$

   ____ $+ 6 = 12$

   So, $12 - 6 =$ ____.

Subtract. Write the related addition fact.

5. 15 − 7 = ____ ____ + ____ = ____	**6.** 18 − 9 = ____ ____ + ____ = ____	**7.** 17 − 4 = ____ ____ + ____ = ____
8. 16 − 12 = ____ ____ + ____ = ____	**9.** 13 − 2 = ____ ____ + ____ = ____	**10.** 15 − 11 = ____ ____ + ____ = ____

Problem Solving

11. There were 15 children reading in the library. Some children went home. 6 children are still in the library. How many children went home?

____ children went home.

Write About It

12. Jack sees 9 butterflies in his garden. He watches 2 fly away. Jack uses a related addition fact to find the number of butterflies left in the garden. He says there are 11 butterflies left. What is Jack's mistake? Explain what he should have done.

_____

_____

_____

_____

Name _____

Think Addition to Subtract

You can think of a related addition fact to subtract.

There are 10 monkeys climbing the trees at a zoo. Then 6 monkeys come down. How many monkeys are still in the trees?

Subtract to find how many monkeys are still in the trees.

$10 - 6 = ?$
$4 + 6 = 10$ ← Use a related addition fact to help you solve the subtraction problem.
So, $10 - 6 = 4.$

There are 4 monkeys still in the trees.

MORE PRACTICE

Subtract. Complete a related addition fact.

1. $9 - 4 = ?$

   ____ $+ 4 = 9$

   So, $9 - 4 =$ ____.

2. $10 - 8 = ?$

   ____ $+ 8 = 10$

   So, $10 - 8 =$ ____.

3. $13 - 7 = ?$

   ____ $+$ ____ $=$ ____

   So, $13 - 7 =$ ____.

4. $11 - 7 = ?$

   ____ $+$ ____ $=$ ____

   So, $11 - 7 =$ ____.

Subtract. Write the related addition fact.

5. $18 - 16 =$ ____

   ____ $+$ ____ $=$ ____

6. $10 - 3 =$ ____

   ____ $+$ ____ $=$ ____

7. $17 - 7 =$ ____

   ____ $+$ ____ $=$ ____

Subtract. Complete a related addition fact.

1. $15 - 8 = ?$

   _____ $+ 8 = 15$

   So, $15 - 8 =$ _____.

2. $14 - 6 = ?$

   _____ $+ 6 = 14$

   So, $14 - 6 =$ _____.

Subtract. Write the related addition fact.

3. $13 - 4 =$ _____

   _____ $+$ _____ $=$ _____

4. $8 - 4 =$ _____

   _____ $+$ _____ $=$ _____

5. $11 - 8 =$ _____

   _____ $+$ _____ $=$ _____

6. $17 - 6 =$ _____

   _____ $+$ _____ $=$ _____

7. $19 - 13 =$ _____

   _____ $+$ _____ $=$ _____

8. $18 - 14 =$ _____

   _____ $+$ _____ $=$ _____

Problem Solving

9. Dalia makes 11 pancakes. Her family eats 4.
   Then Dalia makes 6 more pancakes.
   How many pancakes are there now?

   There are _____ pancakes now.

Write About It

10. Tell what you know about the related addition facts
    for these two subtraction facts.

    $13 - 8 = ?$ $13 - 5 = ?$

    _____

    _____

Name _____

Use Addition to Check

Objectives
- Use mental strategies to add and subtract.
- Use addition to check subtraction.

Math Word
related facts

Jacob makes 15 cups of lemonade. Then he sells 6 cups of lemonade. How many cups of lemonade does Jacob have now?

Subtract to find how many cups Jacob has now.

$15 - 6 = ?$

$15 - 6 = 9$

You can use a related addition fact to check the answer.

$15 - 6 = 9$

$9 + 6 = 15$

Add the number you subtracted to your answer.

If the sum is the number you started with, your answer is correct.

These facts use the same numbers. They are related facts.

The answer is correct.

▷ Jacob now has 9 cups of lemonade.

PRACTICE

Subtract. Write the related addition fact.

1. $12 - 7 =$ _____

   ___ + ___ = ___

2. $13 - 5 =$ _____

   ___ + ___ = ___

3. $15 - 8 =$ _____

   ___ + ___ = ___

Subtract. Write the related addition fact to check your answer.

4. $13 - 8 =$ _____

_____ + _____ = _____

5. $16 - 9 =$ _____

_____ + _____ = _____

6. $14 - 5 =$ _____

_____ + _____ = _____

Problem Solving

7. Emma picks 16 flowers. She gives 7 flowers to Leah and 4 flowers to Jo. How many flowers does Emma have left?

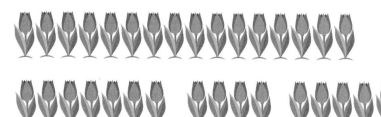

Emma has _____ flowers left.

Solve. Check.

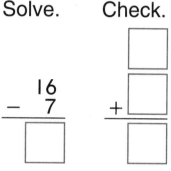

$$\begin{array}{r} 16 \\ -\ 7 \\ \hline \square \end{array} \qquad +\ \square$$

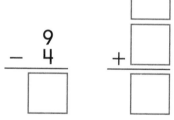

$$\begin{array}{r} 9 \\ -\ 4 \\ \hline \square \end{array} \qquad +\ \square$$

Write About It

8. Andrew subtracts $13 - 4$ and says that the difference is 17. Explain how to use addition to tell whether Andrew's answer is correct.

_____

_____

_____

_____

Name _____

Use Addition to Check

You can use addition to check subtraction.

$$15 - 6 = ?$$
$$15 - 6 = 9$$

You can use the related addition fact to check the subtraction.

$$15 - 6 = 9$$

These facts use the same numbers.

$$9 + 6 = 15$$

| Add the number you subtracted to your answer. | If the sum is the number you started with, it is correct. |

They are related facts.

MORE PRACTICE

Subtract. Write the related addition fact to check your answer.

1. $9 - 5 =$ ____

   ____ $+$ ____ $=$ ____

2. $12 - 7 =$ ____

   ____ $+$ ____ $=$ ____

3. $14 - 7 =$ ____

   ____ $+$ ____ $=$ ____

4.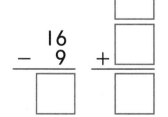
$$\begin{array}{r} 16 \\ -\ \ 9 \\ \hline \end{array}$$

5.
$$\begin{array}{r} 13 \\ -\ \ 7 \\ \hline \end{array}$$

6.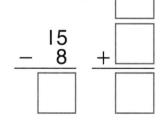
$$\begin{array}{r} 15 \\ -\ \ 8 \\ \hline \end{array}$$

Subtract. Write the related addition fact to check your answer.

1. 10 − 3 = ____

____ + ____ = ____

2. 12 − 8 = ____

____ + ____ = ____

3. 14 − 9 = ____

____ + ____ = ____

4.
```
   14      □
 −  6   + □
 ──────
   □       □
```

5.
```
   16      □
 −  7   + □
 ──────
   □       □
```

6.
```
   15      □
 −  9   + □
 ──────
   □       □
```

Problem Solving

7. There are 15 apples in a bag. 6 are red. The rest are green. How many green apples are in the bag? Complete the subtraction and write the related fact.

There are ____ green apples in the bag.

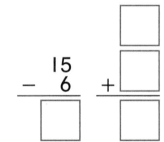

Write About It

8. José subtracts to find 14 − 5 = 9. He adds to check his subtraction: 14 + 9 = 5. He says that the subtraction was wrong because 14 + 9 is not 5. What mistake did José make?

_____

_____

_____

Name _____

Solve for Unknowns

Objective
▪ Use drawings and equations to find the unknown.

Math Words
bar model
subtraction
  equation
unknown

Nick has 12 marbles. He gives some to his brother. Now Nick has 9 marbles. How many marbles does Nick give to his brother?

Subtract to find how many.

Draw a bar model.

whole

12

Write a subtraction equation with an unknown.

?	9
part	**part**

12 − ? = 9

Find the unknown part.

Count up from the lesser number to the greater number.

9 ⟶ 10, 11, 12   So, 12 − 3 = 9.

3 numbers

▷ Nick gives his brother 3 marbles.

PRACTICE

Solve for the unknown.

1. 15 − ____ = 7

whole

15

7	?
part	**part**

2. 12 − ____ = 4

3. 16 − ____ = 5

4. 9 − ____ = 6

Solve for the unknown.

5. $11 - \underline{\quad} = 4$ | 6. $14 - \underline{\quad} = 9$ | 7. $10 - \underline{\quad} = 4$

8.
$$\begin{array}{r} 16 \\ -\ \Box \\ \hline 7 \end{array}$$

9.
$$\begin{array}{r} 8 \\ -\ \Box \\ \hline 5 \end{array}$$

10.
$$\begin{array}{r} 13 \\ -\ \Box \\ \hline 2 \end{array}$$

11.
$$\begin{array}{r} 20 \\ -\ \Box \\ \hline 4 \end{array}$$

Problem Solving

12. Look at the subtraction equation $18 - ? = 6$.
Complete the bar model to find the unknown.
Then complete the subtraction equation.

$18 - \underline{\quad} = 6$

whole

____	

____	?
part	**part**

Write About It

13. Howie had 14 coins. He loses some coins and now he has 5 coins left. Howie thinks he should use one of these equations to find how many coins he loses.

$14 - ? = 5 \qquad 14 - 5 = ?$

Explain which equation Howie should use.

_____

_____

_____

Solve for Unknowns

Solve for the unknown.

Draw a bar model.

Write a subtraction equation with an unknown.

$$12 - ? = 9$$

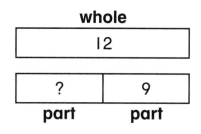

whole

| 12 |

| ? | 9 |

part   **part**

Find the unknown number.

Count up from the lesser number to the greater number.

$9 \longrightarrow \underbrace{10, 11, 12}_{3 \text{ numbers}}$ So, $12 - 3 = 9$.

The unknown number is 3.

MORE PRACTICE

Solve for the unknown.

1. $10 - \underline{} = 5$	2. $15 - \underline{} = 6$	3. $13 - \underline{} = 9$
4. $14 - \underline{} = 3$	5. $11 - \underline{} = 2$	6. $20 - \underline{} = 3$

| 7. $\begin{array}{r} 19 \\ -\ \square \\ \hline 15 \end{array}$ | 8. $\begin{array}{r} 16 \\ -\ \square \\ \hline 3 \end{array}$ | 9. $\begin{array}{r} 9 \\ -\ \square \\ \hline 2 \end{array}$ | 10. $\begin{array}{r} 17 \\ -\ \square \\ \hline 10 \end{array}$ |

Solve for the unknown.

1. $12 - \underline{\quad} = 6$

2. $16 - \underline{\quad} = 14$

3. $17 - \underline{\quad} = 12$

4. $\begin{array}{r} 14 \\ -\ \square \\ \hline 5 \end{array}$

5. $\begin{array}{r} 13 \\ -\ \square \\ \hline 0 \end{array}$

6. $\begin{array}{r} 19 \\ -\ \square \\ \hline 5 \end{array}$

7. $\begin{array}{r} 15 \\ -\ \square \\ \hline 10 \end{array}$

Problem Solving

8. There are 15 children in the library. Some of the children are girls. 8 of the children are boys.
   How many girls are there?
   Write a subtraction equation. Then solve.

   $\underline{\quad} - ? = \underline{\quad}$

   $\underline{\quad} - \underline{\quad} = \underline{\quad}$

   There are $\underline{\quad}$ girls in the library.

Write About It

9. A store has 7 balloons. The store sells some of the balloons. There are 3 balloons left. Katie says that the store sells 10 balloons. What is Katie's error?

   _____

   _____

   _____

   _____

Name _____

Make 10 to Subtract

Clara has 14 balloons at her party.
She gives away 6 balloons to her guests.
How many balloons does Clara have now?

You can use the Make 10 strategy to
find a difference.

$$14 - 6 = ?$$

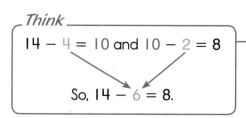

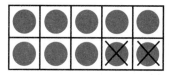 

Clara now has 8 balloons.

Objective
- Use the Make 10 strategy to subtract.

Math Words
difference
Make 10

PRACTICE

Subtract by making 10. Use the ten-frames to help.

1. $15 - 8 = ?$

   $15 - \underline{} = 10$

   $10 - 3 = \underline{}$

   So, $15 - 8 = \underline{}$.

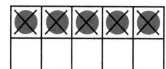

2. $17 - 9 = ?$

   $17 - \underline{} = 10$

   $10 - 2 = \underline{}$

   So, $17 - 9 = \underline{}$.

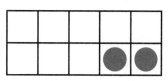 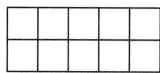

Subtract by making 10.

3. 11 − 4 = ____   **4.** 14 − 5 = ____   **5.** 18 − 9 = ____

6. 13
      − 9
      _____

7. 14
      − 6
      _____

8. 15
      − 9
      _____

9. 12
      − 7
      _____

Problem Solving

10. Ron had 12 feet of ribbon. He uses some to make
a large bow. Now Ron has 9 feet of ribbon left.
How much ribbon does Ron use to make the bow?

Ron uses ____ feet of ribbon.

11. Amelia is riding her bike along a 14-mile trail.
She rides for 8 miles and then takes a break.
How much farther to the end of the trail? Write two
equations to show how to make 10 to subtract.

____ − ____ = 10   10 − ____ = ____

It is ____ more miles to the end of the trail.

Write About It

12. How can you make 10 to find the
difference of 13 − 7?

_____

_____

_____

Name_____

Make 10 to Subtract

You can use the Make 10 strategy to find a difference.

$$14 - 6 = \ ?$$

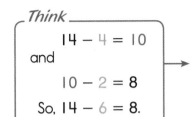

Think_____
14 − 4 = 10
and
10 − 2 = 8
So, 14 − 6 = 8.

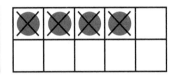

MORE PRACTICE

Subtract by making 10.

1. $14 - 8 = \ ?$

   $14 - 4 = $ ____

   $10 - 4 = $ ____

   So, $14 - 8 = $ ____.

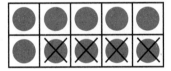 

2. $17 - 9 = $ ____	3. $11 - 3 = $ ____	4. $13 - 5 = $ ____
5. $18 - 9 = $ ____	6. $15 - 7 = $ ____	7. $16 - 6 = $ ____
8. $17 - 8 = $ ____	9. $20 - 14 = $ ____	10. $13 - 7 = $ ____

11. $\begin{array}{r} 12 \\ -\ 7 \\ \hline \end{array}$	12. $\begin{array}{r} 15 \\ -\ 6 \\ \hline \end{array}$	13. $\begin{array}{r} 13 \\ -\ 8 \\ \hline \end{array}$	14. $\begin{array}{r} 14 \\ -\ 7 \\ \hline \end{array}$

Subtract by making 10.

1. 12 − 4 = ____ | 2. 11 − 7 = ____ | 3. 15 − 9 = ____

4. 13
   − 6

5. 14
   − 13

6. 18
   − 11

7. 16
   − 12

Problem Solving

8. Esteban is reading a book with 16 pages.
He has read 9 pages so far. How many
pages does Esteban have left to read?
Write two equations to show how to
make 10 to subtract.

____ − ____ = 10

10 − ____ = ____

Esteban has ____ pages left to read.

Write About It

9. Kyle wants to run 14 miles this week. So far he has
run 3 miles on Monday and 5 miles on Tuesday.
How many more miles does Kyle need to run this week?
Explain how you can make 10 to find the answer.

_____

_____

_____

_____

Problem Solving Read Plan Solve Check
Work Backward

Objectives
- Solve problems working backward.
- Use a variety of strategies to solve problems.

Math Word

work backward

To find the unknown number in an equation, work backward.

$$? + 4 + 5 = 15$$

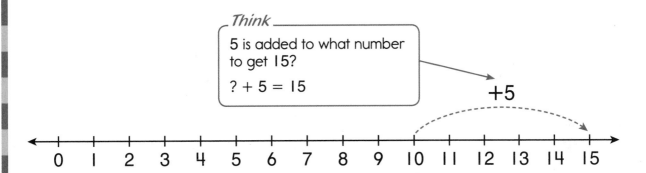

Think

5 is added to what number to get 15?

$$? + 5 = 15$$

$+5$

From the line diagram we see that 5 is added to 10 to get 15.

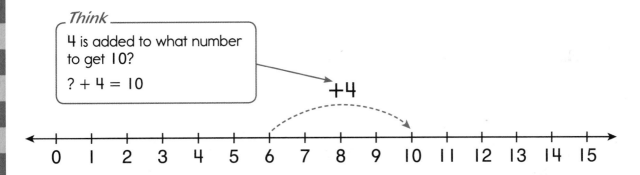

Think

4 is added to what number to get 10?

$$? + 4 = 10$$

$+4$

From the line diagram we see that 4 is added to 6 to get 10.

Since $6 + 4 = 10$, and $10 + 5 = 15$, you know that $6 + 4 + 5 = 15$.

▷ The unknown number is 6.

Find the missing number in each equation.
Use the line diagram to help.

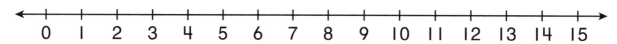

0 1 2 3 4 5 6 7 8 9 10 11 12 13 14 15

1. $8 + 7 - \underline{} = 9$

2. $4 + \underline{} - 3 = 8$

3. $\underline{} + 5 + 3 = 12$

4. $5 + \underline{} - 4 = 9$

Solve.

5. Billy has 5 pennies. He uses 3 pennies to buy a sticker. He finds some more pennies. Then he uses 6 pennies to buy a pencil. Now Billy has 0 pennies left. How many pennies does Billy find?

Billy finds ____ pennies.

6. Carla has 6 shells in her collection. On Monday she finds 2 shells. She finds some more shells on Tuesday. Carla gives 5 shells to her brother. Then she has 7 shells left. How many shells does Carla find on Tuesday?

Carla finds ____ shells on Tuesday.

Write About It

7. Explain how you solved the problem with Carla's shells.

_____

_____

_____

_____

Name _____

Problem Solving
Work Backward

To find the unknown number in an equation, work backward.

$? + 4 + 5 = 15$

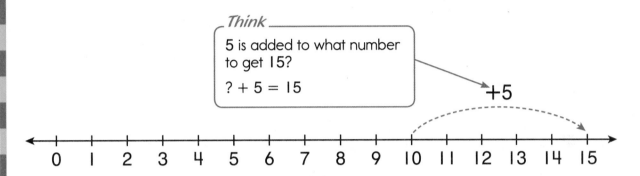

Think
5 is added to what number to get 15?
$? + 5 = 15$

+5

From the line diagram we see that 5 is added to 10 to get 15.

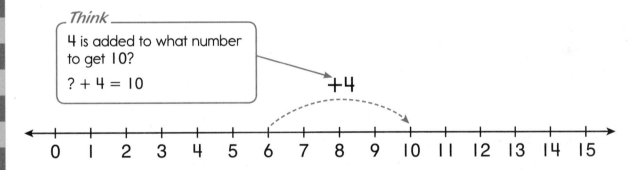

Think
4 is added to what number to get 10?
$? + 4 = 10$

+4

From the line diagram we see that 4 is added to 6 to get 10.

Since $6 + 4 = 10$ and $10 + 5 = 15$, you know that $6 + 4 + 5 = 15$.

The unknown number is 6.

Find the unknown number in each equation.
Use the line diagram to help.

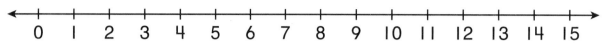

1. $10 - 7 + \underline{\quad} = 9$

2. $8 + \underline{\quad} - 7 = 10$

3. $15 - \underline{\quad} + 5 = 12$

4. $\underline{\quad} + 9 - 8 = 8$

Read each problem. Work backward to solve.

5. Paula picks some apples. She eats 1 apple
   and uses 5 apples to bake a pie. Now Paula has
   12 apples. How many apples does Paula pick?
   Write an equation to represent the problem. Then solve.

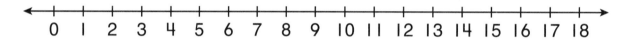

$? - \underline{\quad} - \underline{\quad} = \underline{\quad}$

Paula picks $\underline{\quad}$ apples.

6. Li solves this equation by using the line diagram shown.
   He says the unknown number is 2. Is Li correct? Explain.

$3 + ? - 6 = 5$

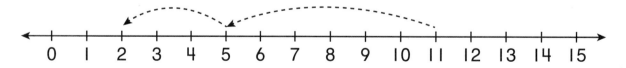

_____

_____

_____

HOMEWORK

**Find the unknown number in each equation.
Use the line diagram to help you.**

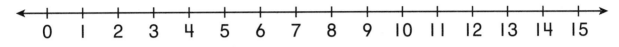

1. $14 - 6 + \underline{\quad} = 13$

2. $10 + \underline{\quad} - 8 = 9$

3. $\underline{\quad} + 6 - 5 = 14$

4. $7 + \underline{\quad} - 5 = 8$

Problem Solving

5. Ari is playing a board game. After 3 moves he is on
   space 17. Ari's first move was forward 2 spaces, and
   his third move was forward 7 spaces. What was Ari's
   second move? Explain how you found the answer.

_____

_____

_____

6. Leon and Thomas have the same number of cherries. Leon eats 5 of his cherries and has 12 cherries left. Thomas eats 9 of his cherries. How many cherries does Thomas have left?

Thomas has _____ cherries left.

Write About It

7. A store has some bicycles for sale. The clerk brings out 2 more bicycles. Later, the store sells 7 of the bicycles. Now there are 5 bicycles left. How many bicycles were outside to start?

Carla and Sara used different ways to solve this problem.

Carla	Sara
$5 + 7 = 12$	Start Clerk
$12 - 2 = 10$	Sold 
Answer: 10 bicycles were outside to start.	Answer: 3 bicycles were outside to start.

Who has the correct answer? _____

Explain the mistake the other child made.

_____

_____

_____

_____

Subtract.

1. $10 - 1 = $ ____

2. $14 - 7 = $ ____

3. ____ $= 11 - 8$

Count on to find the difference.

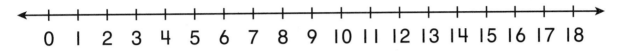

0 1 2 3 4 5 6 7 8 9 10 11 12 13 14 15 16 17 18

4. $9 - 3 = $ ____

5. $12 - 2 = $ ____

6. $18 - 9 = $ ____

For each fact, choose the related subtraction fact.

7. $6 + 5 = 11$

   A. $6 - 5 = 1$

   B. $11 - 4 = 7$

   C. $11 - 5 = 6$

8. $9 + 5 = 14$

   A. $9 - 5 = 4$

   B. $14 - 5 = 9$

   C. $14 - 6 = 8$

Complete the fact family.

9.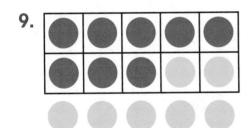

____ $+$ ____ $=$ ____

____ $-$ ____ $=$ ____

____ $+$ ____ $=$ ____

____ $-$ ____ $=$ ____

Subtract. Use a related addition fact.

10. $10 - 3 = $ ____

   ____ $+$ ____ $=$ ____

11. $13 - 9 = $ ____

   ____ $+$ ____ $=$ ____

Solve for the unknown.

12. $8 - \underline{\hspace{1cm}} = 3$

13. $11 - \underline{\hspace{1cm}} = 9$

14. $14 - \underline{\hspace{1cm}} = 6$

Subtract by making 10. Use the ten-frames to help.

15. $16 - 9 = ?$

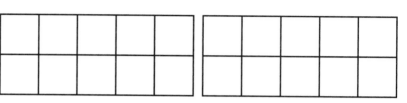

$16 - \underline{\hspace{1cm}} = 10$

$10 - \underline{\hspace{1cm}} = \underline{\hspace{1cm}}$

So, $16 - 9 = \underline{\hspace{1cm}}$.

Solve.

16. There are 7 lemons and 11 limes. How many fewer lemons are there than limes?

   A. 4
   B. 5
   C. 18

17. There are 6 more cups than bowls. There are 15 cups. How many bowls are there?

   A. 8
   B. 9
   C. 21

Work backward to solve.

18. Gia has some string to make bracelets. She uses 7 inches of string to make one bracelet and 6 inches of string to make another bracelet. She has 5 inches of string left. How much string did Gia have at the start? Write an equation to represent the problem. Then solve.

   $? - \underline{\hspace{1cm}} - \underline{\hspace{1cm}} = \underline{\hspace{1cm}}$

   Gia had $\underline{\hspace{1cm}}$ inches of string at the start.

Name _____

**Marc edits videos for the school website.
He cuts out the parts that are too long.
The edited videos are called clips.**

1. The table shows Marc's cuts to three videos.
   Find the length of each clip.

Marc's Videos		
Description	**Video**	**Clip Length (seconds)**
Video: 10 sec Cut: 3 sec	SEC 5 10 15 20 25	$10 - 3 =$ _____
Video: 13 sec Cut: 4 sec	SEC 5 10 15 20 25	$13 - 4 =$ _____
Video: 16 sec Cut: 6 sec	SEC 5 10 15 20 25	$16 - 6 =$ _____

2. Marc edits a video he took in class. He cuts
   9 seconds from the start. Then he cuts 3 seconds
   from the end. The clip is 5 seconds long.
   What was the starting length of the video?

   _____

3. Write a question about cutting a video to
   make a clip. Then solve it.

   _____

   _____

   _____

Name _____

Determine the best answer for each problem.

1. Add.

   $7 + 6 = ?$

   A. 13
   B. 14
   C. 15

2. Subtract.

   $11 - 5 = ?$

   A. 5
   B. 6
   C. 7

3. Write the unknown number in the equation.

   $4 + \underline{\hspace{1cm}} = 12$

4. Write the unknown number in the equation.

   $10 - \underline{\hspace{1cm}} = 3$

5. Which facts are in the same fact family as $13 - 8 = 5$? Check all that apply.

   A. $8 - 5 = 3$
   B. $5 + 8 = 13$
   C. $8 + 5 = 13$
   D. $13 - 4 = 9$
   E. $13 - 5 = 8$

6. Add.

   $$\begin{array}{r} 8 \\ 7 \\ + 3 \\ \hline \end{array}$$

   A. 16
   B. 17
   C. 18

7. Natalie puts 7 books on one shelf and 9 on another shelf. How many books does Natalie put on shelves?

   Natalie puts _____ books on shelves.

8. There are 14 hamsters and 6 gerbils for sale. How many more hamsters are there than gerbils?

   There are _____ more hamsters than gerbils.

Place Value to 100

Some scientists study health and nutrition. They have advice about how to keep your body healthy.

On Your Plate

◆ Eat more of some kinds of foods than others.

◆ Half of your plate should be fruits and vegetables.

On the Move

◆ Do activities that get your heart pumping. Try walking or running.

◆ Three times each week, do activities that make your muscles strong. Try push-ups or gymnastics.

Dear Family,

In this chapter, we will be learning about place value of numbers through 100.

Here are the key  **Math Words** for this chapter:

ones   **equal to (=)**

tens   **greater than (>)**

standard form   **compare**

expanded form

less than (<)

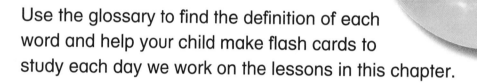

Use the glossary to find the definition of each word and help your child make flash cards to study each day we work on the lessons in this chapter.

During this chapter about place value through 100, we also will be making STEAM (Science, Technology, Engineering, the Arts, and Mathematics) connections about health science and making healthy choices. Read the opening to the chapter together.

Keep Your Skills Sharp

Here is a **Keep Your Skills Sharp** activity to do at home to prepare for this chapter.

Use small objects like beans, pasta, or connecting toy bricks to explore place value. Count out 20 or more objects. Have your child group them into as many piles of ten as possible. Have your child identify the number of tens and the number of leftover ones for each number of objects.

Name _____

Tens and Ones

Objective
- Use tens and ones to show numbers to 100.

Math Words
tens
ones

Lauren has 24 crayons. How many tens and ones are there in 24?

There are 10 ones in 1 ten. To find how many tens and ones in 24, circle groups of 10 crayons.

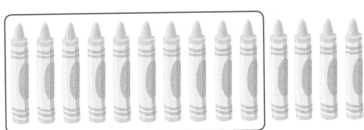

You can circle 2 groups of ten crayons. There are 4 crayons not circled because there are not enough to make another group of ten.

So, there are 2 tens and 4 ones in 24.

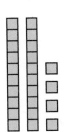

24 ones =
2 tens 4 ones

PRACTICE

Circle groups of ten. Then answer the questions.

1.

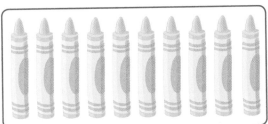

How many tens? _____

How many ones? _____

How many tennis balls in all? _____

Complete the table.

	Model	Number	Tens and Ones
2.		85	_____ tens _____ ones
3.		70	_____ tens _____ ones

Problem Solving

4. Celia reads 34 pages in a book.
   Draw a picture of tens and ones
   to show how many pages
   Celia reads.

5. Jude buys 5 boxes of pencils. Each box has
   10 pencils. He also has 8 pencils in his desk.
   How many pencils does Jude have in all?

   Jude has _____ pencils in all.

Write About It

6. A music teacher sets up 96 chairs for a concert.
   He puts 10 chairs in each row. How many complete
   rows can he make? Explain your answer.

   _____

   _____

Name _____

Expanded Form

Objective
- Write numbers to 100 using expanded form.

Math Words
standard form
expanded form

Brady has 73 baseball cards.

The number 73 is written using standard form.

How is 73 written using expanded form?

Think about how many tens and ones are in 73.

7 tens = 70

The value of the 7 in 73 is 70.

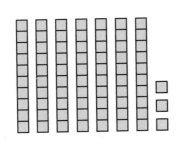

3 ones = 3

The value of the 3 in 73 is 3.

To write a number in expanded form, write an addition expression that adds the values of the tens and ones.

70 + 3

▷ The expanded form of 73 is 70 + 3.

PRACTICE

Write how many tens and ones. Then write the number in expanded form.

1. 48

   ____ tens ____ ones

   ____ + ____

2. 16

   ____ ten ____ ones

   ____ + ____

Complete the table.

	Number	Tens and Ones	Expanded Form
3.	61	_____ tens _____ one	_____ + _____
4.	30	_____ tens _____ ones	_____ + _____
5.	55	_____ tens _____ ones	_____ + _____

Problem Solving

6. Kate uses expanded form to record the number of points she scores in a board game. How many points does Kate score?

   60 + 4

   Kate scores _____ points.

Write About It

7. Lani has 39 colored pencils. She wrote 3 + 9 to show the expanded form of 39. Explain what Lani did wrong. Then show the correct way to write 39 in expanded form.

   _____

   _____

   _____

   _____

Name _____

Compare Numbers

Ava and Mia are having a jump-rope contest. Ava jumps 35 times without stopping and Mia jumps 38 times. Who wins the contest?

Compare the numbers to find which is greater.

Decide if one number is less than (<), greater than (>), or equal to (=) the other number.

35 (?) 38 ← First, look at the tens digits. Compare. The tens digits are the same.

35 (?) 38 ← Next, look at the ones digits. Compare. 5 is less than 8.

35 (<) 38

35 < 38, so Mia wins.

PRACTICE

Compare the tens digits first. If the tens digits are the same, compare the ones digits.

Compare. Write *is less than*, *is equal to*, or *is greater than*. Then write <, =, or >.

1. 48 _____ 27

   48 ◯ 27

2. 34 _____ 45

   34 ◯ 45

3. 26 _____ 26

   26 ◯ 26

4. 91 _____ 96

   91 ◯ 96

Compare. Write $<$, $=$, or $>$.

5. 32 ◯ 52	6. 75 ◯ 57	7. 82 ◯ 84
8. 79 ◯ 73	9. 40 ◯ 40	10. 17 ◯ 17
11. 2 ◯ 23	12. 37 ◯ 29	13. 64 ◯ 73

Problem Solving

14. A farmer has 36 goats and 27 sheep. Does the farmer have a greater number of goats or sheep?

The farmer has a greater number of _____.

Write About It

15. Tell how you can use this model to compare 46 and 54.

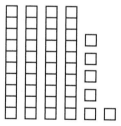 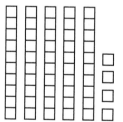

_____

_____

_____

_____

Compare Numbers

Compare to find the greater number.

35 (?) 38

Decide if one number is less than (<), greater than (>), or equal to (=) the other number.

3̲5 (?) 3̲8 ← First, look at the tens digits.
Compare. The tens digits are the same.

3̲5̲ (?) 3̲8̲ ← Next, look at the ones digits.
Compare. 5 is less than 8.

▷ 35 < 38, so 38 is the greater number.

MORE PRACTICE

Compare. Write *is less than*, *is equal to*, or *is greater than*. Then write <, =, or >.

1. 27 _____ 28

    27 ◯ 28

2. 41 _____ 29

    41 ◯ 29

3. 65 _____ 56

    65 ◯ 56

4. 32 _____ 32

    32 ◯ 32

Compare. Write <, =, or >.

5. 74 ◯ 58

6. 16 ◯ 9

7. 50 ◯ 50

8. 88 ◯ 80

9. 23 ◯ 23

10. 68 ◯ 70

Compare. Write <, =, or >.

1. 25 ◯ 35	2. 63 ◯ 59	3. 78 ◯ 78
4. 54 ◯ 45	5. 12 ◯ 31	6. 39 ◯ 40
7. 82 ◯ 82	8. 90 ◯ 99	9. 51 ◯ 52

Problem Solving

10. Raina finds 34 round shells and 28 long shells. Does she find fewer round shells or long shells?

    Raina finds fewer _____ shells.

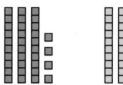

11. Max throws a football 42 feet. Will throws a football farther than Max. Circle the distance that Will could have thrown the football.

    40 feet   42 feet   44 feet

Write About It

12. Ryan compares the numbers 73 and 82. He says that 73 is greater than 82 because 3 is greater than 2. Is Ryan correct? If not, explain his error.

    _____

    _____

    _____

    _____

LESSON 3-3

Write how many tens and ones. Then write the number in expanded form.

Model	Tens and Ones	Expanded Form
I. **39**	____ tens ____ ones	____ + ____

Compare. Write *is less than*, *is equal to*, or *is greater than*. Then write <, =, or >.

2. 37 _____ 33

37 ◯ 33

3. 26 _____ 42

26 ◯ 42

Choose the correct answer.

4. Which number has 3 tens 7 ones?

A. 10

B. 37

C. 73

5. How many tens are in 96?

A. 3 tens

B. 6 tens

C. 9 tens

Compare. Write <, =, or >.

6. 35 ◯ 45 | **7.** 87 ◯ 85 | **8.** 24 ◯ 32

9. 78 ◯ 78 | **10.** 14 ◯ 41 | **11.** 60 ◯ 59

Choose the correct answer.

12. Which are equivalent to 68? Circle all that apply.

 A. 6 tens 8 ones

 B. 8 tens 6 ones

 C. 6 + 8

 D. 60 + 8

 E. 80 + 6

13. Which are equivalent to 50 + 1? Circle all that apply.

 A. 1 ten 5 ones

 B. 5 tens 0 ones

 C. 5 tens 1 one

 D. 15

 E. 51

Solve.

14. Pedro buys 2 black markers. He also buys 3 packs with 10 colored markers in each. How many markers does Pedro buy in all?

Pedro buys _____ markers.

15. Maddie has 90¢. She wants to buy a bow for her costume. Circle the bow or bows she could buy. Explain how you found your answer.

95¢

80¢

89¢

_____

_____

_____

Name _____

Order Numbers Within 100

Objective
- Order numbers within 100.

Math Words
least
greatest

Three friends are on the same soccer team. Karen wears number 27, Lia wears number 26, and Emma wears number 28. They line up in counting order. How do the girls line up?

You can use a number chart to put numbers in counting order.

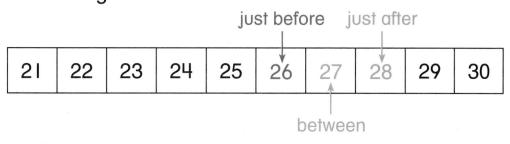

just before   just after

| 21 | 22 | 23 | 24 | 25 | 26 | 27 | 28 | 29 | 30 |

between

26 is just before 27.
26 is 1 less than 27.

27 is between 26 and 28.

28 is just after 27.
28 is 1 more than 27.

26, 27, 28 are in counting order from least to greatest.

▷ Lia is first in line, Karen is next, and Emma is last.

PRACTICE

Write the number that is just before, just after, or between.

1. 45, _____	2. _____, 19	3. 39, _____	4. _____, 90
5. _____, 65	6. 25, _____	7. _____, 51	8. 77, _____
9. 35, _____, 37	10. 18, _____, 20	11. 49, _____, 51	

Complete the number chart.

12.

51	___	53	___	___	56	___	58	59	___

13.

___	___	13	___	15	16	___	___	19	20

Write the numbers in order from least to greatest.

14. 53, 55, 52, 54

_____

15. 27, 26, 29, 28

_____

16. 79, 81, 80, 78

_____

17. 42, 40, 39, 41

_____

Problem Solving

18. Justin's favorite number is just before 64 and just after 62. What is Justin's favorite number?

Justin's favorite number is ____.

Write About It

19. Mason says he read more than 42 pages but fewer than 38 pages. Is this possible? Explain.

_____

_____

_____

Name _____

Order Numbers Within 100

You can use a number chart to order numbers.

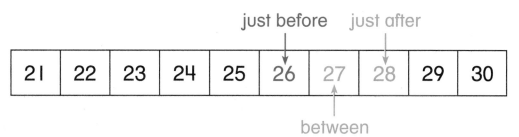

just before   just after

| 21 | 22 | 23 | 24 | 25 | 26 | 27 | 28 | 29 | 30 |

between

26, 27, 28 are in counting order from least to greatest.

MORE PRACTICE

Write the number that is just before, just after, or between.

1. ____, 22	2. 45, ____	3. ____, 17	4. 93, ____
5. 86, ____	6. ____, 30	7. 51, ____	8. ____, 78

9. 61, ____, 63	10. 39, ____, 41	11. 58, ____, 60

Complete the number chart.

12.

| ____ | 42 | ____ | 44 | ____ | 46 | 47 | 48 | ____ | ____ |

13.

| 91 | ____ | 93 | ____ | ____ | 96 | ____ | 98 | 99 | ____ |

Write the number that is just before, just after, or between.

1. 42, _____	2. _____, 18	3. 31, _____	4. _____, 94
5. 19, _____, 21	6. 80, _____, 82	7. 69, _____, 71

Write the numbers in order from least to greatest.

8. 68, 70, 69, 71

_____

9. 15, 12, 13, 14

_____

Problem Solving

10. Three children are standing in a line. Adam is 51 inches tall, Ken is 49 inches tall, and Marc is 50 inches tall. Write their names in order from shortest child to tallest child.

_____

Write About It

11. Grace compares three 2-digit numbers. She knows which number is greatest without even looking at the ones digits. Tell what you know about the tens digits of the numbers. How do you know?

_____

_____

_____

Name _____

Counting Patterns by 2s, 5s, and 10s

Ellie has 6 boxes of chalk. There are 5 pieces of chalk in each box. How many pieces of chalk does Ellie have in all?

You can use a counting pattern. Skip count forward by 5s to find how many pieces of chalk Ellie has in all.

1	2	3	4	5	6	7	8	9	10
11	12	13	14	15	16	17	18	19	20
21	22	23	24	25	26	27	28	29	30

There are 6 boxes, so count by 5s six times: 5, 10, 15, 20, 25, 30.

▷ Ellie has 30 pieces of chalk in all.

A hundred chart can help you count forward or back by 2s, 5s, and 10s.

Look for a pattern.

1	2	3	4	5	6	7	8	9	10
11	12	13	14	15	16	17	18	19	20
21	22	23	24	25	26	27	28	29	30
31	32	33	34	35	36	37	38	39	40
41	42	43	44	45	46	47	48	49	50
51	52	53	54	55	56	57	58	59	60
61	62	63	64	65	66	67	68	69	70
71	72	73	74	75	76	77	78	79	80
81	82	83	84	85	86	87	88	89	90
91	92	93	94	95	96	97	98	99	100

Count forward by 2s from 13:
13, 15, 17, 19

Count back by 5s from 45:
45, 40, 35, 30

Count forward by 10s from 52:
52, 62, 72, 82

Write the missing numbers in the pattern.
Count forward or back by 2s, 5s, or 10s.

1. 63, _____, 59, _____, _____, 53

2. 70, 75, _____, 85, _____, _____

3. 80, 70, _____, _____, _____, 30

4. 34, 44, _____, 64, _____, _____

Problem Solving

5. Rex makes 12 stacks with 2 flyers in each. He makes
   5 stacks with 10 flyers in each. How many flyers does
   Rex make in all? Explain how you can use counting
   patterns to find the answer.

   _____

   _____

   _____

Write About It

6. Kevin counts back, beginning with the number 54.
   All of the numbers he says have 0, 2, 4, 6, or 8 in
   the ones place. Did Kevin count back by 2s, 5s, or
   10s? Tell how you know.

   _____

   _____

   _____

Counting Patterns by 2s, 5s, and 10s

A hundred chart can help you count forward
or back by 2s, 5s, and 10s.

1	2	3	4	5	6	7	8	9	10
11	12	13	14	15	16	17	18	19	20
21	22	23	24	25	26	27	28	29	30
31	32	33	34	35	36	37	38	39	40
41	42	43	44	45	46	47	48	49	50
51	52	53	54	55	56	57	58	59	60
61	62	63	64	65	66	67	68	69	70
71	72	73	74	75	76	77	78	79	80
81	82	83	84	85	86	87	88	89	90
91	92	93	94	95	96	97	98	99	100

Look for a pattern.

Count forward by 2s
from 13:
13, 15, 17, 19

Count back by 5s
from 45:
45, 40, 35, 30

Count forward by 10s
from 52:
52, 62, 72, 82

MORE PRACTICE

**Write the missing numbers in the pattern.
Count forward or back by 2s, 5s, or 10s.**

1. 71, 61, _____, _____ 31, _____

2. 30, 35, 40, _____, _____, _____

3. 75, 73, _____, 69, _____, _____

Match the pattern with the missing number.

1. 23, 33, 43, ___   75

    44, 42, ___, 38   53

    65, 70, ___, 80   40

Write the missing numbers in the pattern.

2. 53, 58, 63, _____, _____, _____

3. 95, _____, 85, _____, _____, 70

Problem Solving

4. Juan counts back from the number 69. The ones digits of the numbers he says do not change. Circle how Juan skip counted.

    by 2s   by 5s   by 10s

Write About It

5. Tim puts 24 photos in an album. He can fit 2 photos on each page. Tell how you can use a pattern to find how many pages Tim uses in the album.

    _____

    _____

    _____

    _____

Problem Solving 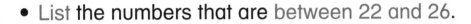 Read 〉 Plan 〉 Solve 〉 Check
Use Logical Reasoning

Objective
▪ Solve problems using logical reasoning.

Math Word
logical reasoning

Jayden lives on Maple Drive.
The number on his house is between 22 and 26.
When you count by 2s from 0, you say the
number. What is Jayden's address?

To find the number, use logical reasoning.

Use the clues in the problem.

? Maple Drive

• List the numbers that are between 22 and 26.

  22, 23, 24, 25, 26

• Circle the number you say when you
  count by 2s from 0.

  23, (24), 25

▷ Jayden's address is 24 Maple Drive.

PRACTICE

Use logical reasoning to solve the problem.

1. Tanya's lives on Elm Road.
   The number in her address is between
   62 and 68. When you count by 5s
   from 0, you say the number.
   What is Tanya's address?

   Tanya's address is _____ Elm Road.

? Elm Road

Use logical reasoning to solve each problem.

2. Raquel is thinking of a mystery number. She says, "It has 2 digits. It is the greatest two-digit number." What is Raquel's mystery number?

   Raquel's number is _____.

3. Dorian is thinking of a mystery number. He says, "It has 2 digits. It is the least two-digit number with a 4 in the tens place." What is Dorian's mystery number?

   Dorian's number is _____.

4. The number of monkeys at a zoo is between 14 and 18. When you count by 2s from 0, you say the number. How many monkeys are at the zoo?

   There are _____ monkeys at the zoo.

Write About It

5. The number of Olivia's address on Main Street has an 8 in the ones place. It is greater than 40. Circle the mailboxes that could be Olivia's. Explain why you did not circle the other mailboxes.

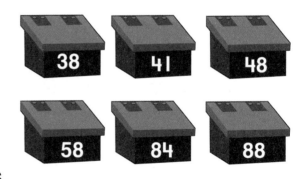

_____

_____

_____

Name _____

Problem Solving
Use Logical Reasoning

The number on Jayden's house number is between 22 and 26. When you count by 2s from 0, you say the number. What is the number on Jayden's house?

Use logical reasoning.

- List the numbers that are between 22 and 26.

  23, 24, 25

- Then circle the number you say when you count by 2s from 0.

  23, (24), 25

> The number on Jayden's house is 24.

MORE PRACTICE

Use logical reasoning to solve each problem.

1. The passcode for Cara's journal has 2 digits. The number is between 60 and 70. The number has a 7 in the ones place. What is the passcode for Cara's journal?

   The passcode is _____.

2. The number of corn plants in a row is between 11 and 19. When you count by 5s from 0, you say the number. How many corn plants are in the row?

   There are _____ corn plants in the row.

Use logical reasoning to solve each problem.

3. The number of Cece's house on
   South Street is between 56 and 66.
   When you count by 10s from 0, you say
   the number. What is Cece's address?

   South Street

   ?

   Cece's address is _____ South Street.

4. Jonah has 6 stamps. Navi has 2 more stamps than
   Jonah. How many stamps do they have in all?

   _____ + _____ = _____

   _____ + _____ = _____

   Jonah and Navi have _____ stamps in all.

5. Prudence is playing a board game. She started at 0,
   and after 3 moves she is on space 12. Her first move
   was forward 5 spaces, and her third move was forward
   3 spaces. What was her second move? Explain.

   _____

   _____

   _____

6. Po is thinking of a mystery number. He says,
   "It is the greatest two-digit number that has a 5 in
   the tens place." What is Po's mystery number?

   Po's number is _____.

HOMEWORK

Use logical reasoning to solve each problem.

1. What is the smallest number that can be made using 2 digits, if none of the digits are zero and none of the digits are repeated?

   _____

2. Hal picks strawberries. The number of strawberries is greater than 70 but less than 80. It has the same number of tens and ones. How many strawberries does Hal pick?

   Hal picks _____ strawberries.

3. Lila is thinking of a mystery number. She says, "It is between 16 and 19. When you count by 2s from 0, you say the number." What is Lila's mystery number?

   Lila's mystery number is _____.

4. Think of your own two-digit mystery number. Complete these clues that would allow a friend to figure out your number.

   My number is between _____ and _____.

   It has a _____ in the ones place.

   My mystery number is _____.

5. Tova's bike lock has a two-digit passcode. The number is between 80 and 90. When you count by 5s from 0, you say the number. What is it?

The passcode is _____.

6. Trent has some trading cards. He buys 8 more and then gives 3 to his brother. If Trent now has 7 cards, how many did he have to start?

Trent had _____ cards to start.

Write About It

7. At a school store, you can win one of these pens. The pen costs more than 15¢. When you count by 10s from 0, you say the cost of the pen. Which pen can you win?

Danny and Leo looked for the answer.

Danny started at 15¢. Then he skip counted 10¢ more.

15¢ + 10¢ = 25¢

Danny circled the pen that cost 25¢.

Leo used the clues.

25¢ and 30¢ are more than 15¢.

He counted by 10s from 0: 10, 20, 30.

Leo circled the pen that cost 30¢.

Who was correct? Circle one name.   Danny   Leo

Describe the error the other child made.

_____

_____

Name_____

Write how many tens and ones. Then write the number in expanded form.

Model	Tens and Ones	Expanded Form
1. 46	_____ tens _____ ones	_____ + _____

Compare. Write <, =, or >.

2. 24 ◯ 27

3. 90 ◯ 90

4. 18 ◯ 34

5. 50 ◯ 49

6. 65 ◯ 56

7. 12 ◯ 21

Choose the correct answer.

8. How many tens are in 34?

   A. 3 tens

   B. 4 tens

   C. 7 tens

9. Which answer shows the expanded form of 47?

   A. 4 + 7

   B. 40 + 7

   C. 70 + 4

Order the numbers from least to greatest.

10. 25, 24, 22, 23

_____

11. 39, 37, 40, 38

_____

12. 49, 51, 50, 48

_____

13. 69, 68, 70, 67

_____

Write the missing numbers in each pattern.
Count forward or back by 2s, 5s, or 10s.

14. 84, 74, _____, _____ 44, _____

15. 15, 20, 25, _____, _____, _____

16. 71, _____, 75, 77, _____, _____

Solve.

17. Sierra plays softball. The number on her jersey is just before the number that is just before 14. What number is on Sierra's jersey?

_____ is the number on Sierra's jersey.

18. Enzo lives on Pine Street. The number in his address is between 44 and 48. When you count by 2s from 0, you say the number. What is Enzo's address?

Enzo's address is _____ Pine Street.

Jason wants to exercise and eat healthier.

1. Jason does 5 minutes of push-ups every day.
How many days will it take him to do exactly 60 minutes'
worth of push-ups? Explain how you know.

_____

_____

2. The table shows nutrition facts for Jason's favorite
snacks. It shows the number of grams of fat, protein,
and sugar in each snack. Your body breaks down fat,
protein, and sugar to get the energy it needs.

For each row, draw a square around the greatest number
of grams and a circle around the least number of grams.

Nutrition Facts for Snacks				
	Yogurt	Cheese	Cupcake	Banana
Fat (grams)	6	12	10	0
Protein (grams)	5	16	2	1
Sugar (grams)	21	1	26	20

3. Which of the snacks has the **least** number of

grams of fat? _____

4. Look at the nutrition labels of your three favorite snacks.
List the snacks in order from least to greatest based
on the number of grams of sugar.

_____

Determine the best answer for each problem.

1. Write the missing number in the equation.

$$13 - \underline{\quad} = 5$$

2. Count by 2s. Write the missing numbers.

50, 52, ____, 56, ____

3. Add.

$$8 + 4 = ?$$

A. 10

B. 11

C. 12

4. Subtract.

$$14 - 5 = ?$$

A. 8

B. 9

C. 11

5. Add.

$$\begin{array}{r} 5 \\ 4 \\ + 6 \\ \hline \end{array}$$

A. 15

B. 16

C. 17

6. Which are the same as 37? Circle all that apply.

A. 10 ones

B. 3 tens 7 ones

C. 7 tens 3 ones

D. 3 + 7

E. 30 + 7

7. Jeremy has 2 chess medals and 9 soccer medals. How many medals does Jeremy have in all?

A. 7 medals

B. 11 medals

C. 12 medals

8. There are 15 raisins in a bowl. Lucy eats 8 raisins. How many raisins are left in the bowl?

There are ____ raisins left in the bowl.

Addition: Two-Digit Numbers

Bridges help us cross canyons, rivers, and bays. Bridges must be strong enough to hold people, cars, and sometimes even trains. That's a lot of weight!

Keep It Simple

♦ A beam bridge is a simple bridge. It can be just a beam held up by piers.

♦ Beam bridges are usually not longer than 85 yards.

Make It Stronger

♦ A suspension bridge has cables stretched over towers. The towers hold most of the weight.

♦ A suspension bridge can be more than 1 mile long.

Dear Family,

In this chapter, we will be learning about adding two-digit numbers.

Here are the key Math Words for this chapter:

model	**regroup**
addend	**place value**
tens	**place-value chart**
ones	**break apart**

The terms *ones*, *tens*, and *addend* are not new to students. Some Math Words are repeated, as they set a foundation for building students' understanding of and fluency with addition. Use the glossary to find the definition of each word and help your child make flash cards to study each day we work on the lessons in this chapter.

During this chapter about adding two-digit numbers, we will also be making STEAM (Science, Technology, Engineering, the Arts, and Mathematics) connections about bridge designs. Read the opening to the chapter together.

Keep Your Skills Sharp

Here is a **Keep Your Skills Sharp** activity to do at home.

Have your child draw a place-value chart with columns labeled *tens* and *ones*. Give your child the ages of several family members. Have your child record the numbers in the chart and then explain why digits are placed in particular columns.

Name _____

Use Models: Add Tens and Ones

The second grade takes a trip to the zoo.
Forty-three children ride on Bus 1.
Twenty-four children ride on Bus 2.
How many children ride buses in all?

Model the addends. Find the sum.

Objective
■ Use models of tens and ones to add without regrouping.

Math Words

model
addend
tens
ones

Model 43. Show
4 tens 3 ones. →

Model 24. Show →
2 tens 4 ones.

tens	ones
6 tens	**7 ones**

tens	ones
4	3
+ 2	4
6	7

▷ 67 children ride buses in all.

PRACTICE

Use models to add. Find the sum.

1. 12
  + 36

tens	ones
____ tens	____ ones

2. 25
  + 14

tens	ones
____ tens	____ ones

3. 32
  + 21

tens	ones
____ tens	____ ones

4. 22
  + 24

tens	ones
____ tens	____ ones

Color the blocks to make a model. Find the sum.

5. 42
    + 14
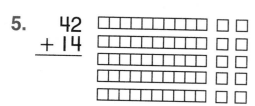

6. 17
    + 22

7. 31
    + 16
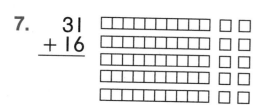

8. 24
    + 34

9. 11
    + 26

10. 33
    + 20

Problem Solving

11. Thirteen children ride camels at a zoo.
    Then 31 more children take camel rides.
    How many children ride camels?

    _____ children ride camels.

—Write About It

12. Explain how you can use models to add 42 + 25.

    _____

    _____

    _____

    _____

Name _____

Use Models: Add Tens and Ones

43 + 24 = ?

Model the addends. Add tens and ones.

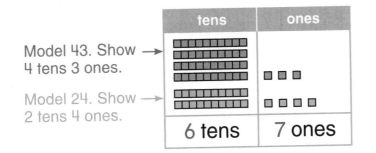

Model 43. Show → 4 tens 3 ones.

Model 24. Show → 2 tens 4 ones.

tens	ones
6 tens	7 ones

	tens	ones
	4	3
+	2	4
	6	7

➤ 43 + 24 = 67

MORE PRACTICE

Use models to add. Find the sum.

1. 31
   + 11

tens	ones
____ tens	____ ones

2. 23
   + 13

tens	ones
____ tens	____ ones

Match each addition problem to the model of the addends.

3.

tens	ones

tens	ones

tens	ones

13 + 11   15 + 11   13 + 12

Use models to add. Find the sum.

1.
$$\begin{array}{r} 15 \\ +\ 22 \\ \hline \end{array}$$

tens	ones
_____ tens	_____ ones

2.
$$\begin{array}{r} 17 \\ +\ 12 \\ \hline \end{array}$$

tens	ones
_____ tens	_____ ones

Color the blocks to model the addends. Find the sum.

3.
$$\begin{array}{r} 11 \\ +\ 48 \\ \hline \end{array}$$

4.
$$\begin{array}{r} 13 \\ +\ 22 \\ \hline \end{array}$$

Problem Solving

5. Fifteen people buy bagels at a bakery.
Then 31 more people buy bagels.
How many people buy bagels in all?
Color the blocks to find the answer.

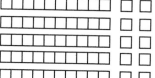

_____ people buy bagels in all.

Write About It

6. Sam says the sum of 33 + 21 is a number greater than 50. Is he correct? Explain how you know.

_____

_____

_____

Name _____

Add Tens and Ones

Jessa picks 31 berries. Tanya picks 52 berries. How many berries do they pick in all?

$31 + 52 = ?$

Write the addends in a place-value chart.

Objective
- Use place-value charts to add without regrouping.

Math Words
addend
place-value chart
tens
ones

First, add the ones.

tens	ones
3	1
+ 5	2
	3

Next, add the tens.

tens	ones
3	1
+ 5	2
8	3

Jessa and Tanya pick 83 berries in all.

PRACTICE

**Add the ones. Then add the tens.
Write the sum.**

1.

tens	ones
2	0
+ 1	1

2.

tens	ones
1	5
+ 2	4

3.

tens	ones
2	2
+ 3	4

4.

tens	ones
1	3
+ 6	2

5.
$$\begin{array}{r} 22 \\ +62 \\ \hline \end{array}$$

6.
$$\begin{array}{r} 48 \\ +30 \\ \hline \end{array}$$

7.
$$\begin{array}{r} 60 \\ +17 \\ \hline \end{array}$$

8.
$$\begin{array}{r} 36 \\ +52 \\ \hline \end{array}$$

9.
$$\begin{array}{r} 42 \\ +57 \\ \hline \end{array}$$

Find the sum.

10. 35 +31	11. 41 +36	12. 73 +25	13. 45 +44	14. 17 +11
15. 33 +12	16. 26 +40	17. 21 +52	18. 26 +13	19. 83 +16

20. **Which problems have a sum of 68?**
    Select all that apply.

    A. 63
+15   **B.** 50
+18   **C.** 14
+55   **D.** 36
+32   **E.** 25
+43

Problem Solving

21. A baker sells 15 loaves of bread in the morning and 32 more loaves in the afternoon. How many loaves are sold in all?

    The baker sells ____ loaves of bread.

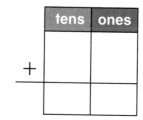

Write About It

22. How does knowing addition facts help you add 35 and 24?

    _____

    _____

    _____

    _____

Name _____

Add Tens and Ones

You can use a place-value chart to add two-digit numbers. Write the addends in a place-value chart.

What is the sum of 31 and 52?

First, add the ones.

tens	ones
3	1
5	2
	3

+

Next, add the tens.

tens	ones
3	1
5	2
8	3

+

▷ $31 + 52 = 83$

MORE PRACTICE

Find the sum.

1. $\begin{array}{r} 26 \\ +22 \\ \hline \end{array}$

2. $\begin{array}{r} 12 \\ +20 \\ \hline \end{array}$

3. $\begin{array}{r} 21 \\ +32 \\ \hline \end{array}$

4. $\begin{array}{r} 24 \\ +21 \\ \hline \end{array}$

5. $\begin{array}{r} 73 \\ +15 \\ \hline \end{array}$

6. $43 + 41 =$ ____

7. $70 + 21 =$ ____

8. $35 + 42 =$ ____

9. **Which problems have a sum of 59?**
   Select all that apply.

   A. $\begin{array}{r} 40 \\ +19 \\ \hline \end{array}$

   B. $\begin{array}{r} 52 \\ +17 \\ \hline \end{array}$

   C. $\begin{array}{r} 34 \\ +25 \\ \hline \end{array}$

   D. $\begin{array}{r} 25 \\ +33 \\ \hline \end{array}$

   E. $\begin{array}{r} 50 \\ +40 \\ \hline \end{array}$

Find the sum.

1. $\begin{array}{r} 31 \\ +25 \\ \hline \end{array}$	2. $\begin{array}{r} 13 \\ +15 \\ \hline \end{array}$	3. $\begin{array}{r} 10 \\ +14 \\ \hline \end{array}$	4. $\begin{array}{r} 22 \\ +35 \\ \hline \end{array}$	5. $\begin{array}{r} 43 \\ +26 \\ \hline \end{array}$
6. $\begin{array}{r} 30 \\ +37 \\ \hline \end{array}$	7. $\begin{array}{r} 45 \\ +41 \\ \hline \end{array}$	8. $\begin{array}{r} 35 \\ +44 \\ \hline \end{array}$	9. $\begin{array}{r} 36 \\ +52 \\ \hline \end{array}$	10. $\begin{array}{r} 73 \\ +24 \\ \hline \end{array}$

Add. Compare the sums. Write >, <, or =.

11. $30 + 10 \bigcirc 20 + 20$

12. $40 + 12 \bigcirc 40 + 11$

13. $15 + 10 \bigcirc 13 + 12$

14. $22 + 44 \bigcirc 23 + 53$

Problem Solving

15. Twenty-five adult tickets and 34 children's tickets are sold for a movie. How many tickets are sold in all?

    _____ tickets are sold in all.

Write About It

16. Aliyah has 14 index cards. She opens a pack of 50 more cards. Explain how to find the number of cards Aliyah has in all.

    _____

    _____

    _____

Use models to add. Color the blocks to model the addends. Find the sum.

1. 46
  + 12

2. 24
  + 23

3. 31
  + 13

4. 17
  + 22

5. A school band has 25 members.
   13 more people join the band.
   How many people are in the band now?
   Color the blocks to make a model to find the answer.

   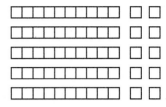

   There are ____ people in the band now.

Which number shows the sum?

6. 12
  + 36

   A. 38
   B. 48
   C. 39
   D. 84

7. 52
  + 13

   A. 55
   B. 56
   C. 65
   D. 74

8. Which two sums have a ones digit of 9?

A. 32
   + 27

B. 57
   + 41

C. 24
   + 63

D. 37
   + 42

9. Which two sums have a tens digit of 8?

A. 42
   + 23

B. 35
   + 51

C. 24
   + 63

D. 22
   + 32

10. Which problems have a sum of 95?
Select all that apply.

A. 43
   + 52

B. 29
   + 30

C. 10
   + 85

D. 24
   + 71

E. 20
   + 65

Solve.

11. A bike rack has 24 spaces. A second bike rack adds 64 spaces. How many bike rack spaces are there now?

There are ____ bike rack spaces now.

Regroup Ones as Tens

Sophia has 3 sheets of 10 stamps each, or 30 stamps in all. Then she buys 14 individual stamps. How many stamps does Sophia have now?

Objective
▪ Regroup ones to make a new ten.

Math Words
model
regroup
ones
tens

Model 3 tens and 14 ones.
Regroup the ones if you can.

There are more than 9 ones. You can regroup the ones.	10 ones = 1 ten Regroup 10 ones as 1 ten.

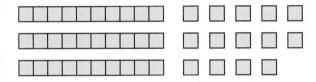

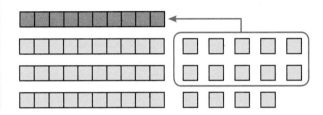

3 tens 14 ones = 4 tens 4 ones = 44

▷ Sophia has 44 stamps now.

PRACTICE

Use models to regroup. Write the new number of tens and ones.

1.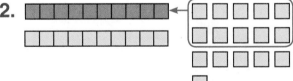

3 tens 12 ones =

___ tens ___ ones

2.

1 ten 16 ones =

___ tens ___ ones

Regroup. Write the new number of tens and ones.

3.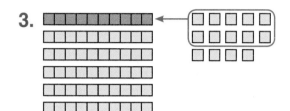

5 tens 14 ones =

___ tens ___ ones

4.

3 tens 17 ones =

___ tens ___ ones

Regroup the ones. Write the new number of tens and ones.

5. 3 tens 11 ones =

___ tens ___ one

6. 1 ten 17 ones =

___ tens ___ ones

Problem Solving

7. Emily has 2 groups of 10 blocks and 13 single blocks. How can she regroup the blocks so there are the greatest number of groups of 10 possible?

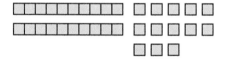

Regroup ___ tens ___ ones as ___ tens ___ ones.

Write About It

8. What happens to the number of tens and ones when 10 ones are regrouped as 1 ten?

_____

_____

Name _____

Regroup Ones as Tens

How can you regroup 3 tens and 14 ones?

There are more than 9 ones. You can regroup the ones.	10 ones = 1 ten Regroup 10 ones as 1 ten.

 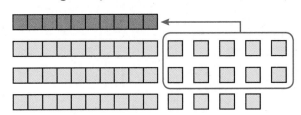

➤ 3 tens 14 ones = 4 tens 4 ones

MORE PRACTICE

Use models to regroup. Write the new number of tens and ones.

1.

5 tens 13 ones =

____ tens ____ ones

2.

4 tens 18 ones =

____ tens ____ ones

Regroup 10 ones as 1 ten. Write the new number of tens and ones.

3. 4 tens 16 ones =

____ tens ____ ones

4. 6 tens 10 ones =

____ tens ____ ones

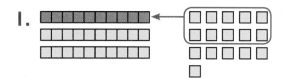

Use models to regroup. Write the new number of tens and ones.

1. 2 tens 16 ones =

_____ tens _____ ones

2. 1 ten 19 ones =

_____ tens _____ ones

Regroup 10 ones as 1 ten. Write the new number of tens and ones.

3. 4 tens 12 ones =

_____ tens _____ ones

4. 2 tens 10 ones =

_____ tens _____ ones

Problem Solving

5. Gus connects 3 groups of 10 cubes each. He also has 12 single cubes. How can he regroup the cubes so there are the greatest number of groups of 10 possible?

Regroup _____ tens _____ ones as _____ tens _____ ones.

Write About It

6. Can you regroup the ones in 1 ten 20 ones? Explain how you know.

_____

_____

Use Models: Two-Digit Addition with Regrouping

Objective
▪ Use models of tens and ones to add with regrouping.

Math Words
model
addend
regroup

Hannah reads a book that has 36 pages.
She reads another book that has 29 pages.
How many pages does Hannah read in all?

Model the addends.
Regroup ones as tens to add.

Model 36 and 29.

tens	ones

$\begin{array}{r} 36 \\ + 29 \\ \hline ? \end{array}$

5 tens	15 ones

There are more than 9 ones.
You need to regroup.

Regroup 10 ones as 1 ten.
15 ones = 1 ten 5 ones

tens	ones

$\begin{array}{r} 36 \\ + 29 \\ \hline 65 \end{array}$

6 tens	5 ones

▷ Hannah reads 65 pages in all.

PRACTICE

Use the models to regroup. Write the sum.

1.

$\begin{array}{r} 28 \\ + 27 \\ \hline \end{array}$

tens	ones

____ tens ____ ones

2.

$\begin{array}{r} 17 \\ + 23 \\ \hline \end{array}$

tens	ones

____ tens ____ ones

Add.

3.

tens	ones

37
+ 25

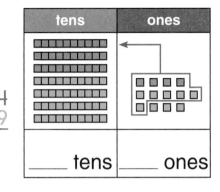

_____ tens _____ ones

4.

tens	ones

24
+ 49

_____ tens _____ ones

Color the blocks to model the addends.
Regroup 10 ones as 1 ten. Write the sum.

5.   35
    + 15

_____ tens _____ ones

6.   26
    + 18

_____ tens _____ ones

Problem Solving

7. Max collects 17 cans of food during a food drive. Ned collects 19 cans of food. How many cans do Max and Ned collect in all? Color the blocks to find the answer.

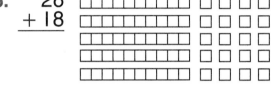

They collect _____ cans of food in all.

Write About It

8. Why do you need to regroup when adding 54 + 27?

_____

_____

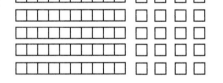

Name_____

Use Models: Two-Digit Addition with Regrouping

$36 + 29 = ?$

You can regroup when adding two-digit numbers.

Model the addends. Regroup ones as tens to add.

Model 36 and 29.

Regroup 10 ones as 1 ten.

15 ones = 1 ten 5 ones

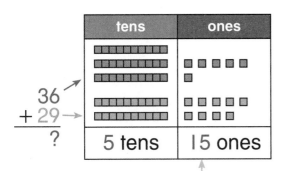

$$\begin{array}{r} 36 \\ + 29 \\ \hline ? \end{array}$$

tens	ones
5 tens	15 ones

There are more than 9 ones. You need to regroup.

tens	ones
6 tens	5 ones

$$\begin{array}{r} 36 \\ + 29 \\ \hline 65 \end{array}$$

$36 + 29 = 65$

MORE PRACTICE

Add. Use the models to regroup.

1.

$$\begin{array}{r} 27 \\ + 15 \end{array}$$

tens	ones
____ tens	____ ones

2.

$$\begin{array}{r} 14 \\ + 26 \end{array}$$

tens	ones
____ tens	____ ones

Add. Use the models to regroup.

1.

tens	ones

$$\begin{array}{r} 25 \\ + 28 \\ \hline \end{array}$$

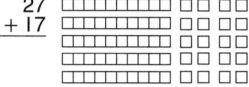

_____ tens _____ ones

2.

tens	ones

$$\begin{array}{r} 39 \\ + 12 \\ \hline \end{array}$$

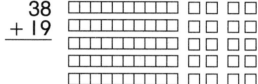

_____ tens _____ ones

**Color the blocks to model the addends.
Regroup 10 ones as 1 ten. Write the sum.**

3. $\begin{array}{r} 27 \\ + 17 \\ \hline \end{array}$

_____ tens _____ ones

4. $\begin{array}{r} 38 \\ + 19 \\ \hline \end{array}$

_____ tens _____ ones

Problem Solving

5. Noah has 28 crayons. Then he gets 27 more crayons. How many crayons does Noah have now?

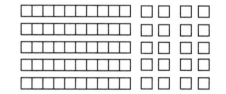

Noah has _____ crayons now.

Write About It

6. Maddie shaded this model to add 13 + 26. She wrote 40 for the sum. What error did Maddie make? Explain.

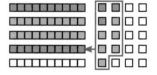

_____

_____

Name _____

Two-Digit Addition with Regrouping

Objective
- Add two-digit numbers with regrouping.

Math Words
addend
place-value chart
regroup

At a farm, Mike picks 25 purple plums and 18 yellow plums. How many plums does Mike pick in all?

Write the addends in a place-value chart.

Regroup 10 ones as 1 ten where needed.

Add the ones. Regroup.

Write the regrouped 10. →

tens	ones
1	
2	5
+ 1	8
	3

Regroup 13 ones as 1 ten 3 ones.

Then add the tens.

tens	ones
1	
2	5
+ 1	8
4	3

▷ Mike picks 43 plums in all.

PRACTICE

Add. Regroup where needed.

1.
tens	ones
2	2
+ 1	9

2.
tens	ones
3	6
+ 3	6

3.
tens	ones
1	5
+ 2	5

4.
tens	ones
6	3
+ 1	5

Add. Regroup where needed.

5. $\downarrow$ 15 $+16$	6. $\downarrow$ 53 $+26$	7. $\downarrow$ 37 $+17$	8. $\downarrow$ 23 $+42$	9. $\downarrow$ 36 $+49$
10. 56 $+17$	11. 68 $+16$	12. 79 $+13$	13. 14 $+68$	14. 28 $+59$

Problem Solving

15. Mia takes 23 plastic bottles and 17 glass bottles to a recycling center. How many bottles does she recycle in all? Solve the equation.

$$\begin{array}{r} 23 \\ +17 \\ \hline \end{array}$$

Mia recycles ____ bottles.

16. A train has 29 riders. At the next stop, 54 more riders get on. How many riders are on the train now?

There are ____ riders on the train now.

Write About It

17. When you add two-digit numbers you sometimes need to regroup. Why is knowing how to add three addends important when regrouping two-digit numbers?

_____

_____

_____

Two-Digit Addition with Regrouping

25 + 18 = ?

Regroup 10 ones as 1 ten where needed.

First, add the ones.

Write the
regrouped 10. →

tens	ones
1	
2	5
+ 1	8
	3

Regroup 13 ones
as 1 ten 3 ones.

Next, add the tens.

tens	ones
1	
2	5
+ 1	8
4	3

25 + 18 = 43

MORE PRACTICE

Add. Regroup where needed.

1. 28 +16	2. 17 +36	3. 21 +39	4. 37 +42	5. 46 +19
6. 72 +19	7. 29 +45	8. 58 +37	9. 28 +52	10. 35 +56

11. In which exercise above was there no need to regroup?

Exercise ____

1. Which exercises require regrouping?
   Select all that apply.

   A. 25
   + 14

   B. 31
   + 19

   C. 24
   + 17

   D. 28
   + 36

   E. 72
   + 26

Add. Regroup where needed.

2. 38
   + 17

3. 42
   + 19

4. 21
   + 38

5. 36
   + 18

6. 43
   + 27

7. 58
   + 29

8. 27
   + 37

9. 55
   + 35

10. 26
    + 47

11. 37
    + 49

Problem Solving

12. There are 27 boxes of apple juice and
    15 boxes of grape juice in a cooler.
    How many boxes of juice are there in all?

    There are _____ juice boxes in all.

Write About It

13. Lauren solved this problem. There are
    24 raisins and 46 nuts in a snack mix packet.
    How many raisins and nuts are there?

    What error did Lauren make?

    Lauren's
    Solution

    2 4
    + 4 6
    ——
    6 0

    _____

    _____

    _____

Name _____

Rewrite Two-Digit Addition

Objectives
- Rewrite two-digit addition problems.
- Add two-digit numbers with regrouping.

Math Words
addend
place value
regroup

You can use place value to line up addends in an addition problem.

Example: 29 + 18 = ?

Rewrite the addends.

Think about place value.

Line up the ones.
Line up the tens.

Add. Regroup
if needed.

29 = 2 tens 9 ones

tens	ones
2	9
+ 1	8

18 = 1 ten 8 ones

tens	ones
1	
2	9
+ 1	8
4	7

29 + 18 = 47

PRACTICE

Rewrite the addends. Then add.
Regroup where needed.

1. 14 + 7

tens	ones
+	

2. 34 + 55

tens	ones
+	

3. 45 + 26

tens	ones
+	

4. 6 + 75

tens	ones
+	

Rewrite the addends. Then add.
Regroup where needed.

5. 14 + 6

$$+ \quad\rule{1cm}{0.4pt}$$

6. 39 + 5

$$+ \quad\rule{1cm}{0.4pt}$$

7. 59 + 29

$$+ \quad\rule{1cm}{0.4pt}$$

8. 36 + 20

$$+ \quad\rule{1cm}{0.4pt}$$

Problem Solving

There are 6 blue balloons and 37 red balloons.

9. Show two different ways to write the addition of 6 and 37.

10. How many balloons are there in all?
Show your work.

There are ____ balloons.

Write About It

11. Choose two practice exercises from this lesson. Explain which problem was easier to add when rewritten. Explain why the other one may not need to be rewritten.

_____

_____

_____

Name _____

Rewrite Two-Digit Addition

$29 + 18 = ?$

You can use place value to line up the addends.

Line up the ones.
Line up the tens.

Add. Regroup
if needed.

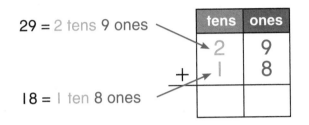

29 = 2 tens 9 ones

tens	ones
2	9
+ 1	8

18 = 1 ten 8 ones

tens	ones
1	
2	9
+ 1	8
4	7

$29 + 18 = 47$

MORE PRACTICE

Rewrite the addends. Add. Regroup where needed.

1. $24 + 8$

$+$

2. $27 + 33$

$+$

3. $39 + 50$

$+$

4. $6 + 36$

$+$

Add. Regroup where needed.
Match the addition to the sum.

5. $7 + 28$ 25

$70 + 28$ 35

$8 + 17$ 97

$80 + 17$ 98

Rewrite the addends. Add. Regroup where needed.

1. 26 + 19

    +

2. 48 + 8

    +

3. 80 + 17

    +

4. 2 + 75

    +

5. 9 + 41

    +

6. 33 + 58

    +

7. 75 + 20

    +

8. 56 + 5

    +

Problem Solving

9. Albert reads 24 pages in his book.
   Then he reads 7 more pages.
   How many pages does Albert read in all?
   Write the addition and solve the problem.

   Albert reads ____ pages in all.

Write About It

10. Colleen had $38 in the bank. She put $5 more
    in the bank. Colleen says that she now has $88.

    What error did Colleen make? How much money
    does she really have in the bank?

    _____

    _____

    _____

Break Apart to Add

Objective
- Break apart numbers to add.

Math Words
break apart
addend
group

There are 45 long-sleeved shirts and
27 short-sleeved shirts on a table at a store.
How many shirts are on the table?

You can break apart the addends. Then you
can group and add the addends in any order.

- Break apart each addend into
  tens and ones.

- Group the tens. Group the ones.

- Add the tens. Add the ones.

- Add the sums.

There are 72 shirts on the table.

$$45 + 27$$

$$40 + 5 + 20 + 7$$

$$40 + 20 + 5 + 7$$

$$60 + 12$$

$$72$$

PRACTICE

Find the missing numbers. Break apart to add.

1. $16 + 38$

   $10 + 6 + \underline{\quad} + 8$

   $10 + 30 + 6 + 8$

   $\underline{\quad} + \underline{\quad}$

   $\underline{\quad}$

2. $29 + 11$

   $20 + \underline{\quad} + 10 + \underline{\quad}$

   $20 + 10 + \underline{\quad} + \underline{\quad}$

   $\underline{\quad} + \underline{\quad}$

   $\underline{\quad}$

After you break apart
the addends, group the
tens first. Group the
ones next. Then add!

Find the missing numbers. Break apart to add.

3. 26 + 35

    ___ + 6 + ___ + 5

    ___ + ___ + 6 + 5

       ___ + ___

       ___

4. 38 + 47

   30 + ___ + 40 + ___

   30 + 40 + ___ + ___

       ___ + ___

       ___

Problem Solving

5. There are 19 hats and 24 scarves in the lost-and-found box. How many hats and scarves are in the box in all? Break apart the numbers to solve.

    There are ___ hats and scarves in the box.

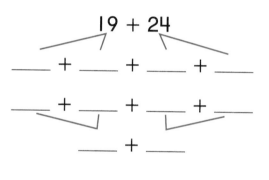

19 + 24

___ + ___ + ___ + ___

___ + ___ + ___ + ___

   ___ + ___

   ___

Write About It

6. Why is adding 49 + 32 the same as adding 40 + 30 + 9 + 2? What is the sum?

    _____

    _____

    _____

    _____

Name_____

Break Apart to Add

$45 + 27 = ?$

You can break apart the addends.
You can group and add the addends
in any order.

$$45 + 27$$

- Break apart the addends. ⟶ $40 + 5 + 20 + 7$

- Group the tens. Group the ones. ⟶ $40 + 20 + 5 + 7$

- Add the sums. ⟶ $60 + 12$

➤ $45 + 27 = 72$

$$72$$

MORE PRACTICE

Find the missing numbers. Break apart to add.

1. $28 + 15$

____ $+ 8 +$ ____ $+ 5$

____ $+$ ____ $+ 8 + 5$

____ $+$ ____

____

2. $47 + 53$

$40 +$ ____ $+ 50 +$ ____

$40 + 50 +$ ____ $+$ ____

____ $+$ ____

____

Circle the addition problems with the same sum.

3. $24 + 36$ $20 + 40 + 3 + 6$ $20 + 30 + 4 + 6$

4. $40 + 30 + 2 + 6$ $42 + 36$ $20 + 60 + 4 + 3$

**Find the missing numbers. Break apart to add.
Then write the sum.**

1.
$$57 + 37$$
____ + 7 + ____ + 7

____ + ____ + 7 + 7

____ + ____

____

2.
$$46 + 39$$
40 + ____ + 30 + ____

40 + 30 + ____ + ____

____ + ____

____

Problem Solving

3. There were 14 cats and 27 kittens adopted last week. How many cats and kittens were adopted in all? Break apart to solve.

There were ____ cats and kittens adopted.

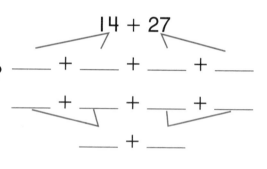

$$14 + 27$$
____ + ____ + ____ + ____

____ + ____ + ____ + ____

____ + ____

____

Write About It

4. Hayden added 32 + 59. His work is shown. What error did Hayden make?

_____

_____

_____

_____

Hayden's Work

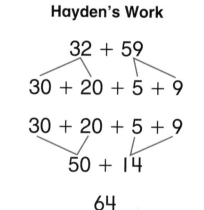

$$32 + 59$$
30 + 20 + 5 + 9

30 + 20 + 5 + 9

50 + 14

64

Name _____

Three Addends

There were 13 people on a bus.
At the next stop, 21 people got on.
At Pine Park, 8 more people got on.
How many people are on the bus now?

Add: 13 + 21 + 8 = ?

Rewrite the problem. Line up the tens and ones.

Add the ones.

tens	ones
1	
1	3
2	1
+	8
	2

Add the tens.

tens	ones
1	
1	3
2	1
+	8
4	2

3 + 1 + 8 = 12.
Regroup 12 ones
as 1 ten 2 ones.

There are 42 people on the bus now.

PRACTICE

Find the sum. Regroup where needed.

1.

tens	ones
6	0
2	7
+	4

2.

tens	ones
1	8
4	0
+ 2	1

3.

tens	ones
3	4
2	1
+ 3	8

4.

tens	ones
5	8
1	9
+ 2	0

Find the sum. Regroup where needed.

5. 24 14 + 8	6. 57 13 +20	7. 35 12 +34	8. 25 31 +23	9. 9 22 +26
10. 38 11 + 5	11. 40 7 +36	12. 14 23 +20	13. 23 26 +23	14. 37 10 +29

Which problems require regrouping?
Select all that apply.

15. **A.** 40
17
+21

B. 25
31
+14

C. 13
30
+ 8

D. 38
21
+10

Problem Solving

16. Marta collects 22 leaves in the park.
Hailey and Lola collect 36 leaves each.
How many leaves do they collect in all?

22
36
+36

They collect ____ leaves in all.

Write About It

17. How is adding three two-digit numbers similar to
adding two two-digit numbers?

_____

_____

_____

Name _____

Three Addends

$13 + 21 + 8 = ?$

Rewrite the problem. Line up the tens and ones.

Add the ones.   Add the tens.

tens	ones
1	
1	3
2	1
+	8
	2

tens	ones
1	
1	3
2	1
+	8
4	2

$3 + 1 + 8 = 12$.
Regroup 12 ones
as 1 ten 2 ones.

$13 + 21 + 8 = 42$

MORE PRACTICE

Find the sum. Regroup where needed.

1.
```
   24
   12
 + 16
```

2.
```
   43
   17
 + 25
```

3.
```
   27
   12
 + 22
```

4.
```
   20
   13
 +  5
```

5.
```
   24
   21
 + 33
```

6.
```
    9
   25
 + 24
```

7.
```
   36
   10
 + 34
```

8.
```
   25
   16
 + 31
```

9.
```
   43
   32
 + 12
```

10.
```
   39
   30
 + 27
```

Find the sum. Regroup where needed.

1.	13 12 + 15	2.	30 16 + 7	3.	12 23 + 21	4.	22 26 + 15	5.	33 6 + 20
6.	26 4 + 23	7.	33 12 + 34	8.	23 39 + 20	9.	43 31 + 14	10.	38 31 + 25

Problem Solving

11. On Friday morning 44 people take a boat ride on a lake. Then, on Friday afternoon, 25 people take a boat ride. On Friday night 13 people take a boat ride. How many people take a boat ride on Friday?

$$\begin{array}{r} 44 \\ 25 \\ + 13 \\ \hline \end{array}$$

On Friday, ____ people take a boat ride.

Write About It

12. Josh added 23 + 2 + 32 and got 67. His work is shown. What error did Josh make?

_____

_____

_____

_____

$$\begin{array}{r} {}^{1} \\ 23 \\ 2 \\ + 32 \\ \hline 67 \end{array}$$

Name _____

Four Addends

Objective
▪ Add four addends.

Math Words
addend
grouping
digit

A farmer has 24 goats, 16 sheep, 17 horses, and 8 turkeys. How many animals does the farmer have?

Add: 24 + 16 + 17 + 8 = ?

Rewrite the problem. Line up the tens and ones. Grouping digits can help you add.

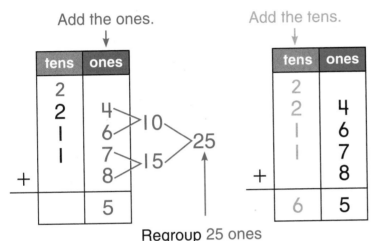

Regroup 25 ones as 2 tens 5 ones.

▷ The farmer has 65 animals.

PRACTICE

Find the sum. Regroup where needed.

1.

tens	ones
2	0
1	1
1	2
+	5

2.

tens	ones
2	8
1	2
2	3
+	2

3.

tens	ones
2	5
1	6
2	8
+	2

4.

tens	ones
2	2
1	4
1	0
+ 2	7

Find the sum. Regroup where needed.

5.
```
  20
  25
  14
+ 11
```

6.
```
  13
  22
  21
+ 23
```

7.
```
  17
  15
  23
+  7
```

8.
```
  29
  51
   8
+ 10
```

9.
```
  34
   6
  17
+  4
```

10.
```
  23
  14
  30
+  5
```

11.
```
  28
  30
   7
+ 21
```

12.
```
  62
  21
  10
+  5
```

13.
```
  23
  25
  12
+ 19
```

14.
```
  48
   8
  26
+ 12
```

Problem Solving

15. Cedric collects 24 pine cones. Kareem collects 28 pine cones. Mike and Leon collect 15 pine cones each. How many pine cones do the four children collect?

They collect _____ pine cones in all.

Write About It

16. Your teacher asks you to find the sum of 12, 23, 47, and 8. What can you do to make the addition easier?

_____

_____

_____

_____

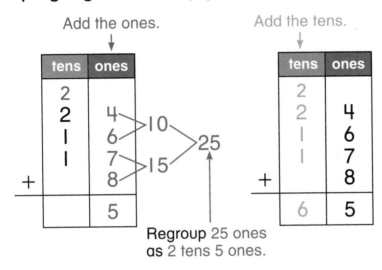

Name _____

Four Addends

24 + 16 + 17 + 8 = ?

Rewrite the problem. Line up the tens and ones.
Grouping digits can help you add.

Add the ones.

Add the tens.

tens	ones
2	
2	4
1	6
1	7
+	8
	5

4 + 6 = 10
7 + 8 = 15
10 + 15 = 25

Regroup 25 ones
as 2 tens 5 ones.

tens	ones
2	
2	4
1	6
1	7
+	8
6	5

24 + 16 + 17 + 8 = 65

MORE PRACTICE

Find the sum. Regroup where needed.

1.	2.	3.	4.	5.
25	30	17	42	12
15	7	31	14	21
11	12	10	9	13
+ 9	+ 18	+ 21	+ 11	+ 14

6. In which exercise above did you need to
regroup 20 ones as 2 tens?

Exercise _____.

Find the sum. Regroup where needed.

1.	2.	3.	4.	5.
50 17 13 + 9	13 12 23 +20	16 44 7 +13	24 21 13 +19	23 15 23 +15

6. **In which exercises do you need to regroup 20 ones as 2 tens? Select all that apply.**

A.	B.	C.	D.	E.
33 21 16 +22	45 8 23 +11	23 18 37 + 2	51 19 5 +24	19 11 48 + 6

Problem Solving

7. Dylan has 22 blue marbles, 17 red marbles, 20 green marbles, and 8 purple marbles. How many marbles does Dylan have in all? Show your work.

   Dylan has ____ marbles.

Write About It

8. Ivy added 28 + 16 + 12 + 8 and got 54. Her work is shown. What error did Ivy make?

   _____

   _____

   _____

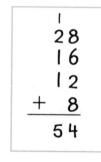

```
    1
   28
   16
   12
 +  8
   54
```

Name_____

Problem Solving ❭Read❭❭Plan❭❭Solve❭❭Check❭
Find Needed Information

A summer camp has 12 cabins. Sixteen campers are in Cabin A and 15 campers are in Cabin B. How many campers are in Cabins A and B?

• What does the question ask?	The question asks for the number of campers in Cabins A and B.
• Look for helpful information.	Look for number names and numbers in standard form. Sixteen campers are in Cabin A and 15 campers are in Cabin B.
• What information is not needed?	A summer camp has 12 cabins. The question does not ask about the number of cabins.
• Solve. Add: 16 + 15 = ?	$\begin{array}{r} 1 \\ 16 \\ +\ 15 \\ \hline 31 \end{array}$

❭ There are 31 campers in Cabins A and B.

Find the needed information to solve each problem. Circle the helpful numbers. Show your work.

Sometimes every number is helpful.

1. Bus A has 28 riders. Bus B has 32 riders. Bus C has 27 riders. How many riders are on those three buses?

   There are ____ riders on those buses.

2. Eighteen rolls of tape are in a storage closet. A teacher puts 7 more rolls of tape in the closet. Each roll has 30 yards of tape. How many rolls of tape are in the closet now?

   There are ____ rolls of tape in the closet.

3. David lives on a road that has has 24 houses. Javier lives on a road that has 18 houses, with 62 people living in those houses. How many houses are on the roads where David and Javier live? Show your work.

   ____ houses

Write About It

4. Look at the problem that asks about the houses on David's and Javier's roads. How did you decide which information was needed to solve it?

   _____

   _____

Name _____

Problem Solving
Find Needed Information

A summer camp has 12 cabins. Sixteen campers
are in Cabin A and 15 campers are in Cabin B.
How many campers are in Cabins A and B?

• What does the question ask?	The question asks for the number of campers in Cabins A and B.
• Look for helpful information.	(Sixteen) campers are in Cabin A and (15) campers are in Cabin B.
• What information is not needed?	A summer camp has 12 cabins.
• Solve.	16 + 15 = 31

▷ There are 31 campers in Cabins A and B.

MORE PRACTICE

**Find the needed information to solve the problem.
Circle the helpful numbers. Show your work.**

1. Seventeen adults and 24 children try out for a
   local chorus. The tryouts last 60 minutes.
   How many people try out for the chorus?

   _____ people try out for the chorus.

Find the needed information in each problem. Then solve.

2. Nia and Jocelyn are adding words to the classroom Word Wall. Nia adds 3 words, then 8 words, and then 5 words. Jocelyn adds 9 fewer words than Nia does. How many words does Jocelyn add?

   Step 1: _____

   Step 2: _____

   Jocelyn adds ____ words to the Word Wall.

3. The number of Keecia's address on Ocean Drive is between 94 and 98. When you count by 2s from 90, you say the number. What is the number of Keecia's address?

   Keecia's address is ____ Ocean Drive.

4. Cooper has some grapes in his bowl. He puts 4 more grapes in his bowl and then gives 6 to his brother. If there are now 8 grapes in Cooper's bowl, how many did he have to start? Explain.

   Work backward.

   _____

   _____

   _____

   _____

Name _____

HOMEWORK

Find the needed information. Then solve.

1. Adam makes 12 turkey sandwiches, 9 tuna sandwiches, and 15 cheese sandwiches for a picnic. How many sandwiches does Adam make in all?

   Show your work.

   Adam makes _____ sandwiches in all.

2. Molly sells single flowers from a bucket. There are 18 red roses, 24 pink roses, and 36 carnations in her bucket. How many roses are in the bucket?

   Show your work.

   There are _____ roses.

   > What information is helpful?

3. Levi and Dan are playing a game with number cubes. Each child tosses 3 number cubes and finds the sum of the dots. Both boys get the same sum. How many dots are on Dan's third number cube?

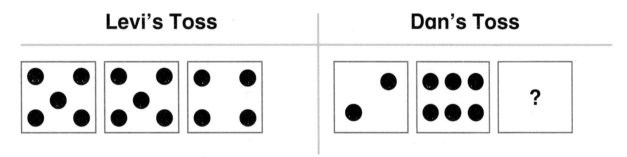

Levi's Toss	Dan's Toss

   There are _____ dots on Dan's third number cube.

4. Joey does 8 cartwheels. His sister Julia does 5 more cartwheels than Joey. How many cartwheels do Joey and Julia do in all? Show your work.

Step 1: _____

Step 2: _____

Joey and Julia do _____ cartwheels in all.

5. Members of the swim team practice for 30 minutes. Eric swims 20 laps, Hakeem swims 28 laps, and Rob swims 16 laps. How many laps do the three boys swim in all?

Eric, Hakeem, and Rob swim _____ laps in all.

Write About It

6. Eva and Gaby try to solve this problem.

   There are 18 classes at an elementary school. Three of the classes are second-grade classes. There are 25 students in each class. How many second-grade students are at the school?

Eva's Work	Gaby's Work
1 25 25 + 25 75	1 18 + 25 43

   Who found the correct answer?
   Circle one name.   Eva   Gaby

   Describe the error the other child made.

   _____

   _____

   _____

Name _____

Use models to add.
Regroup where needed.

1.

tens	ones

36
+ 23

_____ tens | _____ ones

2.

tens	ones

1
19
+ 27

_____ tens | _____ ones

Regroup the ones. Write the new number
of tens and ones.

3. 6 tens 13 ones =

_____ tens _____ ones

4. 7 tens 15 ones =

_____ tens _____ ones

5. Which two sums are greater than 50?
Justify your reasoning by showing
each sum.

A.　 35
　　+ 22

B.　 26
　　+ 23

C.　 25
　　+ 17

D.　 45
　　+ 36

Rewrite the addends. Add. Regroup where needed.

6. 24 + 17

+

7. 46 + 8

+

8. 50 + 28

+

Find the missing numbers. Break apart to add.

9. $59 + 38$

$50 + \underline{} + 30 + \underline{}$

$50 + 30 + \underline{} + \underline{}$

$\underline{} + 17$

$\underline{}$

10. $15 + 27$

$\underline{} + 5 + \underline{} + 7$

$\underline{} + \underline{} + 5 + 7$

$\underline{} + \underline{}$

$\underline{}$

Which number shows the sum?

11.
```
   44
   25
 + 14
```
A. 73
B. 78
C. 83
D. 93

12.
```
   14
   26
   13
 +  8
```
A. 48
B. 85
C. 60
D. 61

Use the information to answer questions 13–14.

There are 65 books in the classroom library. Twelve students borrow a book on Monday and 19 students borrow a book on Tuesday.

13. Circle the numbers that are helpful to find out how many books were borrowed on Monday and Tuesday.

    Write them here. _____

14. How many books were borrowed?
    Explain how you found your answer.

    _____ books were borrowed.

    _____

    _____

Name _____

Ada makes a beam bridge. She uses wooden blocks as piers. She makes a cardboard beam.

Ada uses soup cans as weights. Each can of soup weighs 15 ounces.

1. Ada puts one can on top. When she puts a second can on top, the beam bends. Describe how much weight the bridge holds without bending. Show your work.

   It holds 15 ounces, but not _____ ounces.

---

2. Ada cuts a shorter strip of cardboard. The new bridge supports 3 cans. It does not support 4 cans without bending. How much weight does the bridge hold? Show your work.

   It holds _____ ounces, but not _____ ounces.

> **Fun fact:** When the piers are closer together, the bridge is stronger!

---

3. Next, Ada cuts pieces of string to make cables for a suspension bridge. She uses 26 pieces of string to make one side of the bridge. How many pieces of string does she need to make **both sides** of the bridge? Explain.

   _____

   _____

   _____

   _____

Name _____

Determine the best answer for each problem.

1. Add.

   $5 + 7 = ?$

   A. 11
   B. 12
   C. 13

2. Subtract.

   $17 - 9 = ?$

   A. 6
   B. 7
   C. 8

3. Write the missing number in the equation.

   $11 - \underline{\hspace{1cm}} = 7$

4. Write a related addition fact for $6 + 8 = 14$.

   $\underline{\hspace{1cm}} + \underline{\hspace{1cm}} = \underline{\hspace{1cm}}$

5. Add.

   $\begin{array}{r} 25 \\ + 39 \\ \hline \end{array}$

   A. 54
   B. 64
   C. 65

6. Which amounts have the same value as 82? Select all that apply.

   A. 10 ones
   B. 2 tens 8 ones
   C. 8 tens 2 ones
   D. $8 + 2$
   E. $80 + 2$

7. There are 13 pears and 6 apples in a bowl. How many more pears are there than apples?

   A. 7
   B. 8
   C. 19

8. There are 14 boys and 15 girls at a spelling bee. How many children are at the spelling bee?

   There are _____ children at the spelling bee.

Subtraction: Two-Digit Numbers

CHAPTER 5

Wild giant pandas live in high mountain areas in China. This panda is eating its favorite food, bamboo!

Big Appetite

♦ Giant pandas spend about 12 hours a day eating. They need to eat 20 to 40 pounds of bamboo each day to get the nutrients they need.

Endangered Animals

♦ The giant panda is an endangered animal. This means there are very few left on earth.

♦ Many people are working to protect endangered animals. Find out how you can help, too!

Dear Family,

In this chapter, we will be learning about subtracting two-digit numbers.

Here are the key Math Words for this chapter:

ones	**break apart**
tens	**subtract**
place value	**two-digit**
regroup	**difference**

Terms such as *ones*, *tens*, and *difference* are not new to students in this chapter. Some Math Words are repeated, as they set a foundation for building students' understanding of and fluency with subtraction.

Use the glossary to find the definition of each word and help your child make flash cards to study throughout the chapter.

During this chapter about subtracting two-digit numbers, we will also be making STEAM (Science, Technology, Engineering, the Arts, and Mathematics) connections about endangered animals. Read the opening to the chapter together.

Keep Your Skills Sharp

Here is a **Keep Your Skills Sharp** activity to do at home.

Give your child a group of 25 small objects, like paper clips or beads. Have your child count the total number of objects. Work together to take away groups of 10 to 15 objects. Have your child count how many objects are left.

Name _____

Use Models: Subtract Tens and Ones

Leah has 47 buttons. She gives 23 away. How many buttons does Leah have left?

Use blocks to model 47. Then take away 23.

First subtract the ones.

Then subtract the tens.

tens	ones
4	7
− 2	3
	4

tens	ones
4	7
− 2	3
2	4

The difference has 2 tens 4 ones.
2 tens 4 ones is the same as 24.

▷ Leah has 24 buttons left.

PRACTICE

Subtract. Use the model to help you.

1.

tens	ones
3	8
− 3	5

2.

tens	ones
6	2
− 5	2

Subtract. Use the model to help you.

3.

tens	ones
5	9
− 1	4

4.

tens	ones
7	7
− 3	6

Problem Solving

5. Carlos is doing his math homework. His sister spills paint on some of the problems. What numbers have paint on them?

____ and ____ have paint on them.

$$
\begin{array}{r} 4\ 4 \\ -\ 2\ \\ \hline 2\ 4 \end{array}
\qquad
\begin{array}{r} 8\ 6 \\ -\ \ \ 3 \\ \hline 6\ 3 \end{array}
$$

Write About It

6. Natalie is subtracting 52 − 12 in the place value chart. She says she doesn't need to write the 0 in the ones column. Is she right? Explain.

tens	ones
5	2
− 1	2
4	

_____

_____

_____

Name _____

Use Models: Subtract Tens and Ones

47 − 23 = ?

Use blocks to model 47.
Then take away 23.

tens	ones

First
subtract
the ones.

tens	ones
4	7
− 2	3
	4

Then
subtract
the tens.

tens	ones
4	7
− 2	3
2	4

47 − 23 = 24

MORE PRACTICE

Subtract. Use the model to help you.

1.

tens	ones

tens	ones
6	9
− 6	7

2.

tens	ones

tens	ones
7	2
− 4	0

Subtract. Use the model to help you.

1.

tens	ones

tens	ones
4	8
− 2	4

2.

tens	ones

tens	ones
3	8
− 2	8

Problem Solving

3. Ella collects 74 acorns and 21 pinecones. How many fewer pinecones does she collect than acorns?

tens	ones
−	

   Fill in the place-value chart to subtract.

   Ella collects _____ fewer pinecones.

Write About It

4. David's book has 56 pages. He reads 34 pages. David uses a model to find how many pages he has left to read.

   Is David's model correct? Explain.

tens	ones

   _____

   _____

   _____

Name _____

Subtract Tens and Ones

A zoo has 69 reptiles and 46 monkeys.
How many more reptiles are there
than monkeys?

You can subtract to find the answer.

Objective
- Subtract two-digit
numbers.

Math Words
ones
tens

First subtract the ones.

tens	ones
6	9
− 4	6
	3

Then subtract the tens.

tens	ones
6	9
− 4	6
2	3

There are 23 more reptiles than monkeys.

PRACTICE

Subtract.

1.

tens	ones
7	3
− 7	1

2.

tens	ones
4	4
− 1	4

3.

tens	ones
6	8
− 5	3

4.

5	4
− 2	2

5.

7	9
− 6	4

6.

8	7
− 2	5

Subtract. Remember: You do not need to write a 0 when there are no tens left.

7.	8.	9.	10.
74 − 21	82 − 50	28 − 23	68 − 52

11.	12.	13.	14.
89 − 57	77 − 54	59 − 55	98 − 31

15.	16.	17.	18.
68 − 14	36 − 25	56 − 53	79 − 43

Problem Solving

19. There were 68 apples on a tree.
Some apples fell off. Now the tree has
45 apples on it. How many apples fell off?

_____ apples fell off.

Write About It

20. Justin and Ang both solved
the same problem.
Write about their answers.

Justin

tens	ones
2	8
− 2	4
0	4

Ang

tens	ones
2	8
− 2	4
	4

_____

_____

_____

Subtract. Use the model to help you.

1.

tens	ones
5	9
− 1	3

2.

tens	ones
6	7
− 3	6

3.

tens	ones
4	8
− 2	8

Subtract.

4.

tens	ones
5	4
− 2	1

5.

tens	ones
6	9
− 6	3

Subtract.

6.
```
  57
- 12
```

7.
```
  64
- 34
```

8.
```
  57
- 53
```

9.
```
  85
- 62
```

10.
```
  67
- 21
```

11.
```
  89
- 85
```

12.
```
  74
- 23
```

13.
```
  98
- 13
```

Solve.

14. Matthew spills juice on his
subtraction homework.
What numbers have juice on them?

_____ and _____ have juice on them.

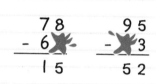
```
  7 8        9 5
-  6        -  3
  1 5        5 2
```

15. An art teacher has 43 paintbrushes.
She passes out 21 paintbrushes to the class.
How many paintbrushes does she have left?

The art teacher has _____ paintbrushes left.

16. There are 48 children playing in the park.
After 12 children go home, 8 other children
come to play in the park. How many
children are playing in the park now?
Explain your answer.

_____

_____

_____

_____

Name _____

Regroup Tens as Ones

You can use models to regroup tens as ones.

Model 18 as 1 ten and 8 ones.
Regroup the ten as ones.

Objective
▪ Use models to regroup
1 ten as 10 ones.

Math Word
regroup

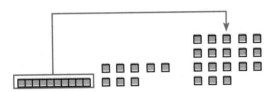

You can regroup, or
trade, 1 ten for 10 ones.

1 ten = 10 ones

> 1 ten   8 ones = 18 ones

PRACTICE

**Use models to regroup.
Write the new number.**

Notice the pattern.
Each time you regroup,
there is 1 fewer ten and
10 more ones!

1.

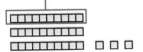

2 tens 0 ones   =   _____ ten _____ ones

2.

3 tens 3 ones   =   _____ tens _____ ones

3.

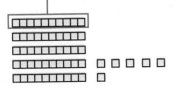 

5 tens 6 ones   =   _____ tens _____ ones

Regroup I ten as 10 ones. Write the new number.

4. I ten 2 ones =

_____ tens _____ ones

5. 2 tens 6 ones =

_____ ten _____ ones

6. 9 tens 4 ones =

_____ tens _____ ones

7. 4 tens 9 ones =

_____ tens _____ ones

8. 5 tens 7 ones =

_____ tens _____ ones

9. 6 tens 3 ones =

_____ tens _____ ones

Problem Solving

10. Jin is building towers of blocks of 10. So far he has made 7 towers and has another 15 blocks. When Jin has built as many towers as possible, how many towers and blocks will he have?

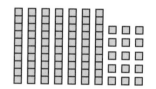

_____ towers and _____ blocks

Write About It

11. Explain all the ways you could regroup 4 tens 7 ones.

_____

_____

_____

_____

Name _____

Regroup Tens as Ones

You can use a model to regroup tens as ones.

Model 18 as 1 ten 8 ones.
Then trade the ten for 10 ones.

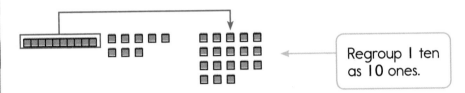

Regroup 1 ten as 10 ones.

1 ten 8 ones = 18 ones

MORE PRACTICE

Use models to regroup. Write the new number.

1.

2 tens 5 ones   =   _____ ten _____ ones

2.

4 tens 8 ones   =   _____ tens _____ ones

3.

5 tens 2 ones   =   _____ tens _____ ones

Regroup I ten as 10 ones. Write the new number.

1. 2 tens I one =

   ____ ten ____ ones

2. 8 tens 9 ones =

   ____ tens ____ ones

3. 9 tens 5 ones =

   ____ tens ____ ones

4. 5 tens 4 ones =

   ____ ten ____ ones

Problem Solving

5. Julia's garden has 31 daisies planted in rows of 10.
   She wants to plant 14 more daisies.

   How many daisies will there be?

   _____

   How many complete rows will there be?

   _____

─Write About It ⬦─────────────────────────

6. There are 28 blocks in all. Oscar says the blocks
   can be grouped as I ten and 18 ones. Is he
   correct? Explain why or why not.

   _____

   _____

   _____

   _____

Name_____

Use Models: Two-Digit Subtraction with Regrouping

Objective
■ Use models to subtract two-digit numbers with regrouping.

Math Words
model
subtract
regroup
tens
ones

Alyssa has 31 beads. She uses 17 of them to make a bracelet. How many beads are left?

You can use a regrouping model to subtract.

There are not enough ones to subtract. Regroup 1 ten as 10 ones.

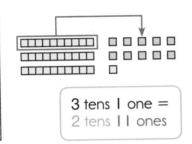

3 tens 1 one = 2 tens 11 ones

Subtract the ones. Then subtract the tens.

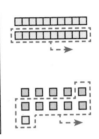

When regrouping, write a small 2 in the tens place and a small 11 in the ones place.

> There are 14 beads left.

PRACTICE

Record the regrouping. Write the difference.

1.

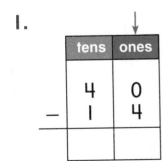
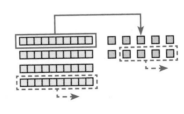

Record the regrouping. Write the difference.

2.

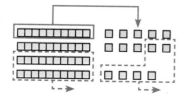

tens	ones
4	4
− 2	6

3.

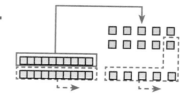

tens	ones
2	5
− 1	6

Problem Solving

4. Choose any two-digit numbers to subtract that would need regrouping. Show the regrouping. Then subtract and write the difference.

64   57

Write About It

5. When do you need to regroup to subtract? When can you subtract without regrouping? Explain how you know.

_____

_____

_____

_____

Name _____

Use Models: Two-Digit Subtraction with Regrouping

You can use a regrouping model to subtract.

$31 - 17 = ?$

There are not enough ones to subtract. Regroup 1 ten as 10 ones.

tens	ones
2	11
3	1
− 1	7

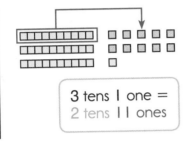

3 tens 1 one =
2 tens 11 ones

Subtract the ones.
Then subtract the tens.

tens	ones
2	11
3	1
− 1	7
1	4

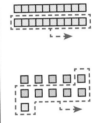

Write a small 2 in the tens place and 11 in the ones place.

$31 - 17 = 14$

MORE PRACTICE

Record the regrouping. Write the difference.

1.

tens	ones
3	2
− 2	5

2.

tens	ones
4	2
− 2	7

Record the regrouping. Write the difference.

1.

tens	ones
5	7
− 1	9

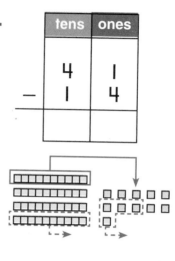

2.

tens	ones
4	1
− 1	4

Problem Solving

3. Choose any two-digit numbers to subtract from that would need regrouping. Then subtract.

☐
− 36
☐

☐
− 49
☐

Write About It

4. A student solved this subtraction problem. What was his error? Explain your reasoning.

tens	ones
	12
7	2̸
− 4	5
3	7

_____

_____

_____

_____

Two-Digit Subtraction with Regrouping

A library has 42 books about ocean animals. 18 of the books are checked out. How many ocean animal books are still at the library?

You can subtract to find how many books are left.

Objectives

• Subtract two-digit numbers with regrouping.
• Subtract one-digit numbers from two-digit numbers with regrouping.

Math Words

subtract
regroup
tens
ones
difference

There are not enough ones to subtract. Regroup 1 ten as 10 ones.

tens	ones
3	12
4	2
– 1	8

First subtract the ones. Then subtract the tens.

tens	ones
3	12
4	2
– 1	8
2	4

There are 24 ocean animal books still at the library.

PRACTICE

Subtract. Show the regrouping.

1.

tens	ones
4	3
–	9

2.

tens	ones
8	0
–	6

3.

tens	ones
7	8
– 4	9

Subtract. Show the regrouping.

4.

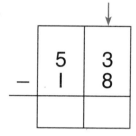

```
    5   3
  - 1   8
  _____
```

5.

```
    7   1
  - 4   4
  _____
```

6.

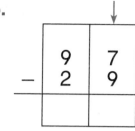

```
    9   7
  - 2   9
  _____
```

7.

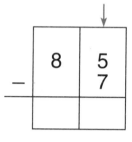

```
    8   5
  -     7
  _____
```

8.

```
    6   8
  - 3   9
  _____
```

9.

```
    5   2
  -     9
  _____
```

Problem Solving

10. Jessica finds 43 shells at the beach.
Addison finds 17 fewer shells than Jessica.
How many shells does Addison find?

Addison finds _____ shells.

Write About It

11. A chef is serving dinner to 36 people. He has
served 19 dinners so far. The chef subtracts
to find how many dinners he has left to serve.
He says he has 27 dinners left.
Explain the mistake the chef made.

```
        16
    3   6̸
  - 1   9
  _____
    2   7
```

_____

_____

_____

Name _____

Two-Digit Subtraction with Regrouping

You can regroup then subtract to find the difference.

42 − 18 = ?

There are not enough
ones to subtract.
Regroup 1 ten as 10 ones.

tens	ones
3	12
4	2
− 1	8

First subtract the ones.
Then subtract the tens.

tens	ones
3	12
4	2
− 1	8
2	4

42 − 18 = 24

MORE PRACTICE

Subtract. Show the regrouping.

1.

	↓
7	4
−	7

2.

	↓
4	8
− 2	9

3.

	↓
6	7
−	8

4.

	↓
9	3
− 1	6

5.

	↓
5	1
− 1	7

6.

	↓
9	5
− 4	9

Subtract. Show the regrouping.

1.
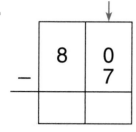

2.
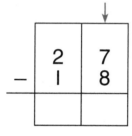

3.
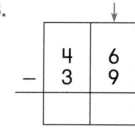

4.

5.
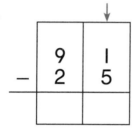

6.

Problem Solving

7. A chef has 90 plates. He uses 28 plates at lunch. How many plates are left?

There are _____ plates left.

Write About It

8. Alan has 41 stickers. His brother has 19 stickers. Alan wants to share his stickers so that they both have the same number. How many stickers should he share? Explain your thinking.

_____

_____

_____

_____

Rewrite Two-Digit Subtraction

Objective
■ Rewrite two-digit subtraction problems from horizontal to vertical form and subtract.

Math Words
subtract
regroup
ones
tens

Luke has 36 books on his shelf.
He has 7 books on his desk.
How many more books are on Luke's shelf?

You can subtract to find how many more books are on the shelf.

$36 - 7 = ?$

Rewrite the subtraction. Think about place value.

Line up the ones.
Line up the tens.

tens	ones
3	6
−	7

Subtract. Regroup if needed.

tens	ones
2	16
~~3~~	~~6~~
−	7
2	9

There are 29 more books on the shelf.

PRACTICE

**Match the subtraction to the rewritten problem.
Then write the difference. Regroup if needed.**

1. $80 - 26$ | 2. $69 - 8$ | 3. $78 - 29$ | 4. $83 - 5$

tens	ones
8	3
−	5

tens	ones
7	8
− 2	9

tens	ones
6	9
−	8

tens	ones
8	0
− 2	6

Rewrite the subtraction. Then write the difference.

5. 52 − 37

6. 43 − 7

7. 77 − 65

8. 97 − 9

9. 58 − 26

10. 67 − 8

11. 72 − 5

12. 81 − 32

Problem Solving

13. Keisha picked 46 strawberries and Mara picked 25 strawberries. They ate 15 of them on the way back home. How many strawberries are left?

    _____ strawberries are left.

Write About It

14. David's work for finding 86 − 7 is shown. Is his answer correct? Explain why or why not.

_____

_____

_____

Name _____

Break Apart to Subtract

Objective
■ Break apart numbers
to subtract.

Math Words
subtract
break apart
tens
ones

You can break apart numbers to subtract.

◆ Break apart the number subtracted to find the difference.

$54 - 9 = ?$	The number subtracted is 9.
	Some ways to break apart 9 are $1 + 8, 2 + 7, 3 + 6, 4 + 5$.
$54 - 9 = ?$ 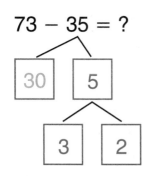	Which way has a number that matches the ones digit in 54?
	Break apart 9 into $4 + 5$.
$54 - 4 = 50$	Subtract 4.
$50 - 5 = 45$	Then subtract 5 more.

➤ So, $54 - 9 = 45$.

◆ You can use place value to break apart the number subtracted.

$73 - 35 = ?$

30 5	Break apart 35 into tens and ones.
3 2	Break apart the ones.
$73 - 30 = 43$	Subtract the tens.
$43 - 3 = 40$	Subtract ones to get to 40.
$40 - 2 = 38$	Then subtract 2 more.

➤ So, $73 - 35 = 38$.

**Break apart numbers to subtract.
Then write the difference.**

1. 52 − 5 = ?

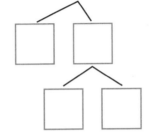

52 − ___ = ___

50 − ___ = ___

52 − 5 = ___

2. 62 − 27 = ?

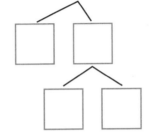

62 − ___ = ___

42 − ___ = ___

40 − 5 = ___

62 − 27 = ___

3. 74 − 28 = ?

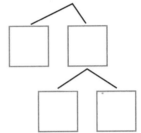

74 − ___ = ___

54 − ___ = ___

50 − 4 = ___

74 − 28 = ___

Problem Solving

4. Ryan has 39 leaves for a science project.
He collects 25 more. Then he gives 7 leaves to
a classmate. How many leaves does he have now?

Ryan now has ___ leaves.

Write About It

5. Explain how to break apart to subtract 51 − 36.

_____

_____

_____

_____

Name _____

Break Apart to Subtract

Use place value to break apart the number subtracted.

$73 - 35 = ?$ | The number subtracted is 35.

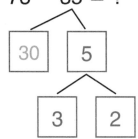

Break apart 35 into *tens* and *ones*.

Break apart the *ones*.

$73 - 30 = 43$ | Subtract the *tens*.

$43 - 3 = 40$ | Subtract *ones* to get to 40.

$40 - 2 = 38$ | Then subtract 2 more.

So, $73 - 35 = 38$.

MORE PRACTICE

Break apart numbers to subtract.

I. $64 - 9 =$ ____

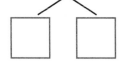

$64 -$ ____ $=$ ____

$60 -$ ____ $=$ ____

2. $58 - 39 =$ ____

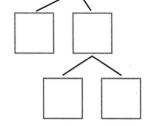

$58 -$ ____ $=$ ____

$28 -$ ____ $=$ ____

$20 - 1 =$ ____

3. $63 - 48 =$ ____

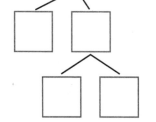

$63 -$ ____ $=$ ____

$23 -$ ____ $=$ ____

$20 - 5 =$ ____

Break apart numbers to subtract.
Then write the difference.

1. 85 – 6 = ____

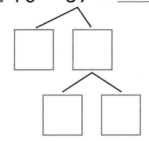

85 – ____ = ____

80 – ____ = ____

2. 42 – 28 = ____

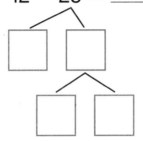

42 – ____ = ____

22 – ____ = ____

20 – 6 = ____

3. 76 – 39 = ____

76 – ____ = ____

46 – ____ = ____

40 – 3 = ____

Problem Solving

4. A school club sells 43 calendars on Monday and 39 calendars on Tuesday. How many more calendars did it sell on Monday than on Tuesday?

____ more calendars

Write About It

5. Tanya wants to subtract 62 – 48. What are some ways she can find the difference? Choose a way and show the work needed to find the difference.

_____

_____

_____

_____

Add to Check

Objective
- Use addition to check subtraction.

Math Words
subtract
add

Lily paints 52 tiles for her art project.
Marta paints 28 tiles for her project.
How many more tiles does Lily paint than Marta?

Subtract to find how many more tiles
Lily paints. Add to check your subtraction.

$$\begin{array}{r} 4\;12 \\ \cancel{5}\;\cancel{2} \\ -\;2\;8 \\ \hline 2\;4 \end{array}$$

$$\begin{array}{r} 1 \\ 2\;4 \\ +\;2\;8 \\ \hline 5\;2 \end{array}$$

← Start with the difference.
← Add the number subtracted.

These numbers are the same.
So, the subtraction is correct.

▷ Lily paints 24 more tiles than Marta.

PRACTICE

Match the subtraction problem to the addition problem you can use to check it.

1. 97 − 63 = 34   29 + 34 = 63

2. 63 − 34 = 29   34 + 63 = 97

Subtract. Complete the addition to check.

3.
$$\begin{array}{r} 89 \\ -\;62 \\ \hline \end{array}$$
$$+\boxed{62}$$
$$\boxed{} \\ \overline{89}$$

4.
$$\begin{array}{r} 42 \\ -\;16 \\ \hline \end{array}$$
$$+\boxed{16}$$
$$\boxed{} \\ \overline{42}$$

5.
$$\begin{array}{r} 76 \\ -\;8 \\ \hline \end{array}$$
$$+\boxed{}$$
$$\boxed{}$$

Subtract. Write the addition to check.

6.
```
  9 8        □
- 2 9   + □
```

7.
```
  6 3        □
- 2 9   + □
```

8.
```
  8 1        □
- 5 6   + □
```

Problem Solving

9. Tina buys 83 bricks to build a path in her garden. She uses only 65 bricks for the path. How many bricks does she have left? Write your answer. Then write an addition equation to check your answer.

Tina has _____ bricks left.

_____ + _____ = _____

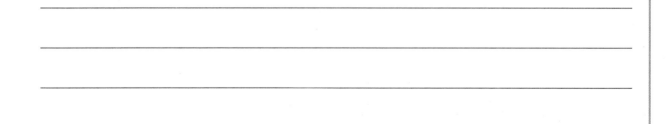

Does your sum match the total number of bricks Tina buys? If so, your answer is correct.

Write About It

10. Sydney subtracts $74 - 36 = 48$.

Check Sydney's answer using addition.
Did Sydney find the correct difference? If not, explain the error she likely made in her subtraction.

_____

_____

_____

_____

Name _____

Problem Solving
Write and Solve an Equation

Objective
- Write and solve an equation for a given problem-solving situation.

Math Words
row
column
diagonal

In this math square puzzle, the numbers in each row, column, and diagonal have a sum of 15. Each of the numbers 1 to 9 is used only once. What are the missing numbers?

You can write and solve an equation to find each missing number.

	7	
	5	
		4

Look for a row, column, or diagonal that already has two numbers.

The sum of 7, 5, and an unknown addend is 15.

- Write an equation to find the unknown addend:

  $7 + 5 + ? = 15$

  12

	7	
	5	
	3	4

- Solve for the unknown addend: $12 + ? = 15$

  $12 + 3 = 15$, so the missing number is 3.

- Write an equation for the bottom row:

  $? + 3 + 4 = 15$

  7

	7	
	5	
8	3	4

- Solve for the unknown addend: $? + 7 = 15$

  $8 + 7 = 15$, so the missing number is 8.

- Write and solve equations to fill in the rest of the boxes to complete the math square.

6	7	2
1	5	9
8	3	4

▷ The missing numbers are shown in the last square.

Solve.

1. Each row, column, and diagonal in this math square puzzle has a sum of 15. Each number, 1 to 9, is used only once. Write and solve equations to complete the math square puzzle.

2		6
	5	

$2 + 5 + \underline{\qquad} = 15$

_____

_____

2. Each shape represents one number. Use the equations to write the number that each shape represents.

⬤ + ⬤ = 10   ⬤ = ____

⬤ + ▲ + ▲ = 9   ▲ = ____

▲ + ■ + ■ + ⬤ = 19   ■ = ____

Write About It

3. Create and solve a math square puzzle that has 5 in the middle square, 2 in one corner and 4 in another corner. Have the numbers in each row, column, and diagonal equal 15. Explain how you solved the puzzle.

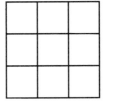

_____

_____

_____

_____

Problem Solving
Write and Solve an Equation

In a math square puzzle, the numbers in each row, column, and diagonal have a sum of 15.

	7	
	5	
	?	4

Each of the numbers 1 to 9 is used only once.

What are the missing numbers in this math square puzzle?

> Look for a row, column, or diagonal with two numbers given.

- Write an equation for the column:

  $7 + 5 + ? = 15$

  12

	7	
	5	
	3	4

- Solve: $12 + ? = 15$

  $12 + 3 = 15$, so the missing number is 3.

- Write an equation for the bottom row:

  $? + 3 + 4 = 15$

  7

	7	
	5	
8	3	4

- Solve: $? + 7 = 15$

  $8 + 7 = 15$, so the missing number is 8.

- Write and solve equations to complete the rest of the math square.

6	7	2
1	5	9
8	3	4

▷ The missing numbers are shown in the last square.

Write and solve equations for each problem.

1. Each row, column, and diagonal in this math square puzzle has a sum of 15. Each number, 1 to 9, is used only once. Write and solve equations to complete the math square puzzle.

4		
	5	
2		

_____

_____

_____

2. Each shape represents one number. Use the equations to write the number that each shape represents.

⬤ + ⬤ = 12

⬤ + ▲ + ▲ = 20

▲ + ◼ + ◼ + ⬤ = 15

⬤ = ____

▲ = ____

◼ = ____

Write About It

3. There are 34 almonds in a bowl now. Earlier Colin ate 9 almonds and then Cooper put 6 more in the bowl. How many almonds were in the bowl to start? Explain your solution. Be sure to show the equations you used to solve the problem.

There were _____ almonds to start.

_____

_____

_____

HOMEWORK

Complete a new math square.

1. Each row, column, and diagonal in this math square puzzle has a sum of 15.
   Each number, 1 to 9, is used only once.
   Write and solve equations to complete the math square puzzle.

8		
	5	9

Read each problem and solve.

2. A zoo has 65 birds now. It adopted 17 new birds last week. How many birds did the zoo have before it adopted the new birds? Write and solve an equation. Then write the answer.

_____ – _____ = _____

The zoo had _____ birds to start.

3. There are 77 boxes of cereal on a store shelf. The store sells 28 boxes in the morning and 19 boxes in the afternoon. How many boxes of cereal are left on the shelf? Write equations to solve the problem. Then write the answer.

Step 1: _____ – _____ = _____

Step 2: _____ – _____ = _____

There are _____ boxes of cereal left on the shelf.

Read each problem and solve.

4. At the end of the day, there are 42 books on a library shelf. Mrs. Patel had added 14 new books and taken away 7 old books during the day. How many books were on the shelf at the start of the day?

_____ books

5. Each shape represents the given number. Write the name of the shape that completes each equation.

★ = 42

● = 23

▲ = 61

■ = 67

▲ − _____ = 38

■ − _____ = 25

★ − _____ = 19

6. Jack added 57 + 34. He wrote 81 for his answer. Tell what Jack did wrong. Then find the correct sum.

_____

_____

Write About It

7. Building A is taller than Building B. Building C is shorter than Building A. Can you order the three buildings by height? Explain.

_____

_____

_____

Name _____

Subtract.

1.
```
    7 | 4
  – 2 | 1
  ———————
```

2.
```
    3 | 8
  – 3 | 3
  ———————
```

Use models to regroup. Write the new number.

3.

7 tens 3 ones   =   ____ tens ____ ones

Record the regrouping. Write the difference.

4.

tens	ones
4	5
– 2	7

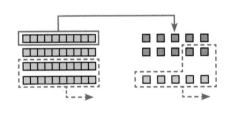

Subtract. Show the regrouping.

5.
```
    5 | 0
  – 3 | 5
  ———————
```

6.
```
    6 | 4
  –   | 8
  ———————
```

Break apart numbers to subtract.
Then write the difference.

7. $76 - 27$

$76 - 20 = \underline{\hphantom{xxx}}$

$56 - \underline{\hphantom{xx}} = \underline{\hphantom{xx}}$

$50 - \underline{\hphantom{xx}} = \underline{\hphantom{xx}}$

$76 - 27 = \underline{\hphantom{xxx}}$

8. $62 - 35$

$62 - 30 = \underline{\hphantom{xxx}}$

$32 - \underline{\hphantom{xx}} = \underline{\hphantom{xx}}$

$30 - \underline{\hphantom{xx}} = \underline{\hphantom{xx}}$

$62 - 35 = \underline{\hphantom{xxx}}$

9. $85 - 49$

$85 - 40 = \underline{\hphantom{xxx}}$

$45 - \underline{\hphantom{xx}} = \underline{\hphantom{xx}}$

$40 - \underline{\hphantom{xx}} = \underline{\hphantom{xx}}$

$85 - 49 = \underline{\hphantom{xxx}}$

Solve.

10. Tyler subtracts 37 from 56 and gets a difference of 19. He wants to use addition to check his answer. Write an addition equation Tyler can use.

$\underline{\hphantom{xxx}} + \underline{\hphantom{xxx}} = \underline{\hphantom{xxx}}$

11. Nicole baked 24 muffins. Eva baked 8 fewer muffins than Nicole. Write and solve an equation to help you find how many muffins in all Nicole and Eva baked.

_____

Nicole and Eva baked _____ muffins in all.

12. Luke wants to rewrite the subtraction $58 - 9$. Explain how he should write the numbers so that he can use place value to subtract correctly.

_____

_____

_____

The table shows information about the eating habits of three giant pandas.

1. Find the difference in the number of pounds of bamboo each panda eats on Monday and Tuesday.

Pounds of Bamboo Eaten			
Panda	Monday	Tuesday	Difference
Ling Ling	33	25	_____
Bei Bei	34	28	_____
Tian Tian	40	27	_____

2. How many more pounds of bamboo did Tian Tian eat on Monday than Bei Bei ate on Tuesday? Explain how you can check your answer, then check it.

_____

_____

_____

3. Another panda named Gu Gu ate 26 pounds of bamboo on Monday and 37 pounds of bamboo on Tuesday.

Use the table and the data about Gu Gu to write two different problems that compare the amounts eaten by the pandas. Then solve the problems and show your work.

_____

_____

_____

Name _____

Determine the best answer for each problem.

1. Add.

   $6 + 5 =$ _____

2. Count on to add.

   $17 + 3 =$ _____

3. Subtract.

   $18 - 9 =$ _____

4. Write the related addition fact.

   $7 + 5 = 12$

   ____ $+$ ____ $=$ ____

5. Which three addition facts have a sum of 17?

   A. $9 + 8$
   B. $7 + 9$
   C. $6 + 11$
   D. $10 + 7$

6. Which two subtraction facts have a difference of 7?

   A. $13 - 5$
   B. $11 - 4$
   C. $12 - 6$
   D. $16 - 9$

7. Complete the fact family.

   $8 + 7 = 15$

   $15 -$ ____ $= 8$

   $7 +$ ____ $= 15$

   ____ $- 8 = 7$

8. How many tens and ones are in 27?

   A. 7 tens 2 ones
   B. 2 tens 7 ones
   C. 1 ten 7 ones
   D. 27 tens 0 ones

9. Choose two ways you can solve $2 + 7 + 3$.

   A. count on
   B. doubles
   C. make ten
   D. doubles plus 1

Measurement

CHAPTER 6

People who study weather are called meteorologists. They tell us about rain, snow, wind, and how hot or cold it is.

Types of Data

♦ Meteorologists use different units—like degrees, miles per hour, and centimeters—to measure each type of data.

Forecasting

♦ Meteorologists can tell us about the day's weather.

♦ What are some questions you might ask about tomorrow's weather?

Dear Family,

In this chapter, we will be learning about estimating and measuring length in both customary and metric units.

Here are the key Math Words for this chapter:

inch (in.)

customary unit

length

foot (ft)

yard (yd)

measuring tape

centimeter (cm)

metric unit

meter (m)

You can use the glossary to find the definition of each word and help your child make flash cards to study throughout this chapter.

During this chapter about measurement, we will also be making STEAM (Science, Technology, Engineering, the Arts, and Mathematics) connections about weather. Read the opening to the chapter together.

Keep Your Skills Sharp

Here is a **Keep Your Skills Sharp** activity to do at home to prepare for this chapter.

Help your child estimate and measure the lengths of several objects in your home using a ruler, yardstick, or measuring tape. Have your child find the difference in the lengths of the objects. Discuss with your child the different types of measurements you use throughout the day.

Name_____

Inches

Mario needs a piece of ribbon about 4 inches long for a project. Can he use this ribbon?

Objective
■ Estimate and measure length to the nearest inch.

Math Words
inch (in.)
customary unit
length
estimate
inch ruler

An inch (in.) is a customary unit of length.

This is 1 inch: ├────────┤.
Estimate the length of the ribbon.

You can measure with an inch ruler to check the estimate.

Line up the left end of the ribbon with the 0-inch mark.

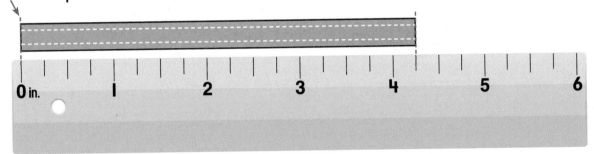

The end of the ribbon is between the 4 and 5.
It is closer to the 4.

⟩ The ribbon is about 4 inches long, so Mario can use it.

PRACTICE

**Estimate the length of the object in inches.
Then use an inch ruler to measure the length.**

1.  Estimate: about _____ inches

   Measure: about _____ inches

**Estimate the length of the object in inches.
Then use an inch ruler to measure the length.**

2.

Estimate: about _____ inches

Measure: about _____ inches

Problem Solving

3. Emily thinks the length of this computer mouse
is about 3 inches. Is she correct? Explain.

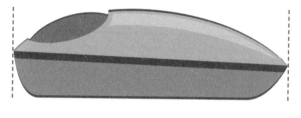

_____

_____

_____

Write About It

4. How can you decide which is the nearest inch
when measuring an object?

_____

_____

_____

Name _____

Inches

You can estimate length in inches.
This is 1 inch: ├───────┤.

Estimate the length of the ribbon.

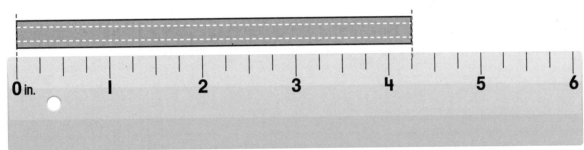

You can use an inch ruler to check your estimate.

⇨ The ruler shows that the ribbon is about 4 inches long.

MORE PRACTICE

**Estimate the length of each object in inches.
Then use an inch ruler to measure the length.**

1.

Estimate: about ____ inches

Measure: about ____ inches

2.

Estimate: about ____ inches

Measure: about ____ inches

**Estimate the length of each object in inches.
Then use an inch ruler to measure the length.**

1.

Estimate: about _____ inches   Measure: about _____ inches

Problem Solving

2. Maddie needs more than 5 inches of string for an
art project. Does she have enough string? Explain.

_____

_____

Write About It

3. Paula measured the length of a ribbon.
She says it is about 2 inches long.
Explain why Paula is incorrect.

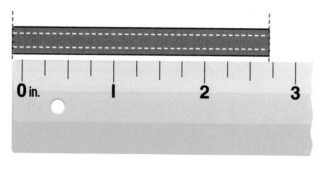

_____

_____

_____

Name _____

Feet and Yards

Abby says the picnic table is about 6 feet long. Cassie says it is about 6 yards long. Who is correct?

Objectives
- Estimate length using feet and yards.
- Measure length to the nearest foot or yard.

Math Words
foot (ft)
ruler
yard (yd)
yardstick

Estimate the length of the picnic table.

I foot (ft) = 12 inches	I yard (yd) = 3 feet = 36 in.

A ruler shows I foot. | A yardstick shows 3 feet or 36 inches.

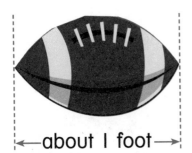

←—about I foot—→

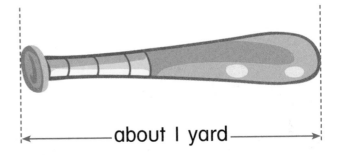

←————about I yard————→

A picnic table could be as long as 6 footballs. | A picnic table is not as long as 6 baseball bats placed end to end.

▷ Abby is correct. The picnic table is about 6 feet long.

PRACTICE

**Estimate the length in feet or yards.
Then measure the object in your classroom.**

1.

Estimate: about _____

Measure: about _____

Estimate the length of your desk or table in feet or yards. Then measure with a ruler or yardstick.

2.

Estimate: about _____

Measure: about _____

Circle the better estimate for each length.

3.

about 3 feet   about 3 yards

4.

about 10 feet   about 10 yards

Problem Solving

5. Estimate the length of a television or screen in your home. Use feet or yards. Explain why it is a good estimate.

_____

_____

Write About It

6. Martin thinks that 2 feet is longer than 1 yard because 2 is greater than 1. Is he correct? Explain.

_____

_____

Name _____

Feet and Yards

You can estimate a length in feet or yards. You can check your estimate with a ruler or yardstick.

1 foot (ft) = 12 inches	1 yard (yd) = 3 feet = 36 in.

A ruler shows 1 foot.

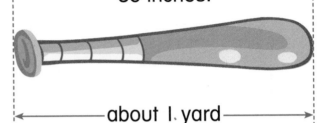

A yardstick shows 3 feet or 36 inches.

←about 1 foot→

A football is about 1 foot long.

←about 1 yard→

A baseball bat is about 1 yard long.

MORE PRACTICE

Circle the better estimate for each length.

1.

about 3 feet   about 3 yards

2.

about 3 feet   about 3 yards

3.

about 4 feet   about 4 yards

4.

about 8 feet   about 8 yards

Estimate the length in feet or yards. Then measure the objects at home with a ruler or yardstick.

1.

Estimate: about _____

Measure: about _____

Circle the better estimate for each length.

2.

about 3 feet   about 3 yards

3.

about 15 feet   about 15 yards

Problem Solving

4. Scott thinks that his bed is about 6 yards long. Is he correct? Explain.

_____

_____

Write About It

5. If you measure the same object in feet and in yards, would the number of units be greater in feet or in yards? Explain.

_____

_____

_____

Customary: Choose Tools and Units of Measure

Objectives
- Choose the best tool to measure length.
- Choose the best customary unit to measure length.

Math Words

inch (in.)
yard (yd)
foot (ft)
measuring tape

Sara wants to measure the length of a planter bed in her garden.

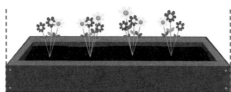

What tool and customary unit should she use?
Think about the tools that measure length.

A ruler can measure in inches.

Use this tool to measure shorter lengths.

A yardstick measures in yards, feet and inches.
A measuring tape can measure in feet and inches.

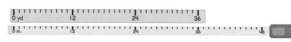

Use these tools to measure longer lengths.

The planter bed is long. Sara should use a yardstick or measuring tape to measure in feet.

PRACTICE

Circle the tool and customary unit you would use to measure the length of the real object.

1.

Tool:	ruler	measuring tape
Unit:	inch	foot

2.

Tool:	ruler	yardstick
Unit:	inch	foot

Write the tool and customary unit you would use to measure the length of the real object.

3.

Tool: _____

Unit: _____

4.

Tool: _____

Unit: _____

Problem Solving

5. Carly wants to measure the entire length of her bedroom floor. She plans to use an inch ruler and measure in inches. Is this the best way for Carly to measure her room? Explain.

_____

_____

_____

Write About It

6. Is a ruler, yardstick, or measuring tape the best tool for measuring a spoon? Explain.

_____

_____

_____

_____

Customary: Choose Tools and Units of Measure

There are different tools and customary units that you can use to measure length.

A ruler can measure in inches.

Use this to measure shorter lengths.

A yardstick measures in yards, feet, and inches.
A measuring tape can measure in feet and inches.

Use these to measure longer lengths.

MORE PRACTICE

Circle the tool and the customary unit you would use to measure the length of the real object.

1.

   Tool: ruler   yardstick

   Unit: inch   yard

2.

   Tool: ruler   yardstick

   Unit: inch   feet

Circle the best answer.

3. Which object's length is best measured with an inch ruler?

   broom   carrot   barn

Write the tool and the customary unit you would use to measure the length of the real object.

1.   Tool: _____

   Unit: _____

2. Tool: _____

   Unit: _____

3. Tool: _____

   Unit: _____

Problem Solving

4. Lucas wants to measure the length of a lunchbox. He plans to measure in feet. Is this the best unit to use? Explain your answer.

_____

_____

Write About It

5. Shayna wants to measure her mother's height using a ruler or a measuring tape. Shayna says she can use either tool. Is she correct? Explain.

_____

_____

_____

Centimeters

Diana is building
a birdhouse. She needs
to use a bolt that is about
5 centimeters long.
Can Diana use this bolt?

Objective
▪ Estimate and measure
length to the nearest
centimeter.

Math Words
centimeter (cm)
metric unit
estimate
centimeter ruler

A centimeter (cm) is a metric unit of length.

This is 1 centimeter: ⊢—⊣.

Estimate the length of the bolt.

The bolt looks about 5 centimeters long.

You can measure with a centimeter ruler to check
the estimate.

Line up the left end of the bolt
with the first mark on the ruler.

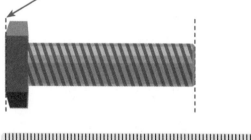

The bolt is between 5 and 6 centimeters long.
It is closer to 5 centimeters.

▷ The bolt is about 5 centimeters long,
so Diana can use it.

Estimate the length of each object in centimeters. Then use a centimeter ruler to measure the length.

Remember: cm means centimeter

1.
   Estimate: about _____ cm

   Measure: about _____ cm

2.

   Estimate: about _____ cm   Measure: about _____ cm

Problem Solving

3. Grace says this piece of yarn is 4 centimeters long. What error did Grace make? What is the correct length of the yarn?

_____

_____

Write About It

4. Your littlest finger is about 1 centimeter wide. Explain how you could use your finger to help you estimate the length of an object.

_____

_____

Centimeters

You can estimate length in centimeters.
You can check your estimate with a
centimeter ruler.

Estimate the length of the bolt.

This is 1 centimeter: .

The bolt looks about 5 centimeters long.

Measure the bolt to check your estimate.

Line up the left end of the bolt with
first mark on the ruler.

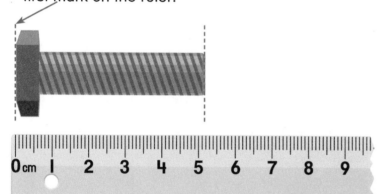

The bolt is between
5 and 6 centimeters
long. It is closer to
5 centimeters.

The ruler shows that the bolt is about
5 centimeters long.

MORE PRACTICE

**Estimate the length of the object in centimeters.
Then use a centimeter ruler to measure the length.**

1.

Estimate: about _____ cm   Measure: about _____ cm

Estimate the length of each object in centimeters. Then use a centimeter ruler to measure the length.

1.

Estimate: about _____ cm

Measure: about _____ cm

2.

Estimate: about _____ cm   Measure: about _____ cm

Problem Solving

3. Chloe needs a string of beads that is at least 7 centimeters long. Is this string of beads long enough? Explain your answer.

_____

_____

Write About It

4. Which is a better estimate for the length of a crayon: 2 centimeters or 10 centimeters? Explain.

_____

_____

_____

Name_____

Meters

Molly says a bathtub is about 20 centimeters long. Talia says it is about 2 meters long. Who is correct?

Objective
▪ Estimate and measure length to the nearest meter.

Math Words
centimeter (cm)
meter (m)
meterstick

Estimate the length of a bathtub.

Your little finger is about 1 centimeter wide.

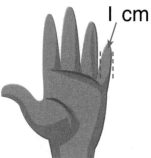

1 cm

A bathtub is longer than 20 fingers placed side by side.

1 meter (m) = 100 centimeters

A meterstick shows 1 meter.

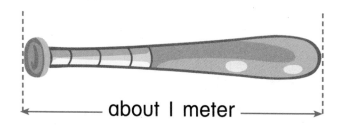

about 1 meter

A bathtub could be as long as 2 baseball bats placed end to end.

Talia is correct. She could use a meterstick to check her estimate.

PRACTICE

Estimate the width. Then measure the object in the classroom with a meterstick or a measuring tape.

1.

Estimate: about _____ meters

Measure: about _____ meters

Estimate the length. Then measure the object in your school with a meterstick or a measuring tape.

2.  Estimate: about _____ meters

Measure: about _____ meters

Circle the best estimate for the length of the real object.

3.  30 meters

3 meters

4.  30 meters

30 centimeters

Problem Solving

5. Choose a vehicle you ride in. Estimate its length in meters. Explain why it is a good estimate.

A vehicle can be a bus, a van, a car, or even a bicycle!

_____

_____

Write About It

6. Explain how you could measure an object that is longer than the length of 1 meterstick.

_____

_____

_____

_____

Name _____

Meters

You can estimate a length in meters.
You can check your estimate with
a meterstick.

I meter (m) = 100 centimeters

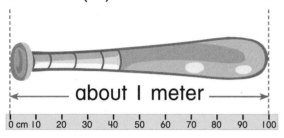

about 1 meter

| 0 cm 10 | 20 | 30 | 40 | 50 | 60 | 70 | 80 | 90 | 100 |

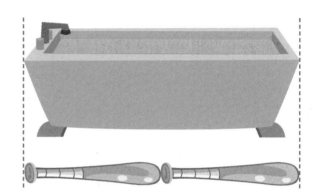

The bathtub is about 2 meters long.

MORE PRACTICE

**Match each real object to the best estimate
of its length.**

1.

2.

3.

I meter   5 meters   20 meters

4. Estimate the length of one wall in your classroom.
   Then measure the wall.

   Estimate: about _____ meters   Measure: about _____ meters

Estimate the length of a sofa. Measure a sofa in your home with a meterstick or a measuring tape.

1. Estimate: about _____ meters

   Measure: about _____ meters

Choose the best metric unit to complete each sentence. Write *centimeters* or *meters*.

2. A school bus is about 13 _____ long.

3. A drinking straw is about 8 _____ long.

Problem Solving

4. Avery measured the length of her kitchen using metersticks as shown. She says the kitchen is 3 meters long. Explain the mistake Avery made.

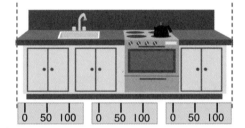

_____

_____

Write About It

5. Nolan has two pieces of ribbon. The red ribbon is 10 centimeters long and the blue ribbon is 2 meters long. Which ribbon is longer? Explain your answer.

_____

_____

Metric: Choose Tools and Units of Measure

Mason wants to measure the length of his nametag.

Objectives
- Choose the best tool to measure length.
- Choose the best metric unit to measure length.

Math Words
centimeter (cm)
meterstick
measuring tape
meter (m)
centimeter ruler

What tool and what metric unit should he use?

A ruler can measure in centimeters.

Use this to measure shorter lengths.

A meterstick can measure in meters and centimeters.

A measuring tape can also measure in centimeters and meters.

Use these to measure longer lengths.

The nametag is short. Mason should use a centimeter ruler and measure in centimeters.

PRACTICE

Circle the tool and metric unit you would use to measure the length of the real object.

1.

Tool:	ruler	meterstick
Unit:	centimeter	meter

2.

Tool:	ruler	meterstick
Unit:	centimeter	meter

Write the tool and metric unit you would use to measure the length of the real object.

3.

Tool: _____

Unit: _____

4.

Tool: _____

Unit: _____

Problem Solving

5. Mitsuko wants to buy a case for a paint set. She plans to use meters to measure the length. Are meters the best metric unit to measure the paint set? Explain.

_____

_____

_____

Write About It

6. Name the tool and unit you would use to measure the length of a library bookshelf. Explain your answer.

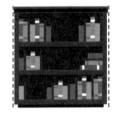

_____

_____

_____

Metric: Choose Tools and Units of Measure

There are different tools and metric units
that you can use to measure length.

A ruler can measure length
in centimeters.

Use this to measure
shorter lengths.

A meterstick can measure length
in meters and centimeters.

A measuring tape can also measure
length in meters and centimeters.

Use these to measure longer lengths.

MORE PRACTICE

**Circle the tool and metric unit you would use
to measure the length of the real object.**

1.

Tool:	ruler	meterstick
Unit:	centimeter	meter

2.

Tool:	ruler	meterstick
Unit:	centimeter	meter

Circle the best answer.

3. Which object's length is best measured
   with a measuring tape?

   bookmark   jump rope   crayon

Write the tool and metric unit you would use to measure the length of the real object.

1.

   Tool: _____

   Unit: _____

2.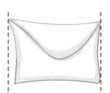

   Tool: _____

   Unit: _____

3.

   Tool: _____

   Unit: _____

Problem Solving

4. Would you use a ruler or a measuring tape to find the length of a garage? Explain.

   _____

   _____

Write About It

5. Name an object you would measure using centimeters and explain why. Then name an object you would measure using meters and explain why.

   _____

   _____

   _____

**Estimate the length of the object in inches.
Then use an inch ruler to measure the length.**

1.

Estimate: about ____ inches   Measure: about ____ inches

**Estimate the length of the object in centimeters.
Then use a centimeter ruler to measure the length.**

2.

Estimate: about ____ cm   Measure: about ____ cm

**Choose the best unit to measure the real object.
Write *inch*, *foot*, or *yard*.**

3. _____

4. _____

**Choose the best unit to measure the length
of the real object. Write *centimeter* or *meter*.**

5.  _____

6. 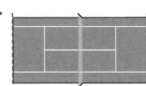 _____

Circle the tool and unit you would use to measure the length of the real object.

7.

Tool:	ruler	measuring tape
Unit:	inches	feet

8.

Tool:	ruler	yardstick
Unit:	inches	feet

9.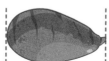

Tool:	ruler	meterstick
Unit:	centimeters	meters

Solve.

10. Tim measures the lengths of three pieces of rope. The lengths are 13 yards, 13 inches, and 13 feet. Which piece of rope is the longest? Explain.

_____

_____

_____

11. Lydia wants to measure the width of her hand in inches, but all she has is a yardstick. Can she still measure the width of her hand? Explain.

_____

_____

_____

Name _____

Measure Using Different Units

◆ Does it take fewer inches or feet to measure the bookcase?

◆ Does it take more centimeters or meters to measure the book?

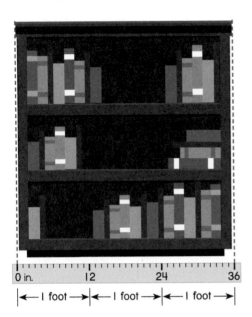

The bookcase measures 3 feet or 36 inches.

$$3 < 36$$

The book measures 20 cm.

$$20 > 1$$

⟹ It takes fewer feet than inches to measure the bookcase. It takes more centimeters than meters to measure the book.

PRACTICE

Measure each real object in meters and in centimeters.

1. The length of your desk

    about ____ meter   about _____ centimeters

Measure each real object in inches and in feet.

2. The length of your math book

   about _____ inches   about _____ foot

3. The length of a window

   about _____ inches   about _____ feet

Problem Solving

4. Nick measures the length of his bedroom in centimeters and then in meters. He says his room is 5 centimeters long. He also says it is 5 meters long. Which measurement is correct? Explain.

   _____

   _____

   _____

   _____

Write About It

5. Alexa says the length of her favorite stuffed animal is 13 feet. What is Alexa's mistake? Explain.

   _____

   _____

   _____

   _____

Measure Using Different Units

You can measure the same object using different units.

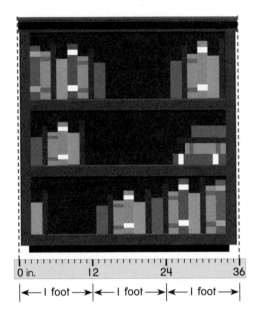

The length of the bookcase is
3 feet or 36 inches.

The book measures
20 centimeters, or less
than 1 meter.

> It takes fewer feet than inches to measure a bookcase.
> It takes more centimeters than meters to measure a book.

MORE PRACTICE

Measure the real object in feet and in inches.

1. The length of a chalkboard or whiteboard

   about ____ feet   about ____ inches

**Measure the real object in centimeters
and in meters.**

2. The classroom wall measures

   about _____ centimeters   about ____ meters

Measure the length of the real object at home.
Use the units shown.

1. The length of a pillow

   about _____ inches   about ___ feet

Circle the correct words to complete the sentence.

2. It takes (more / fewer) meters than centimeters
   to measure a hallway because meters are
   (larger / smaller) than centimeters.

Problem Solving

3. Bea measures the length of a flower patch
   in inches and then in feet. She says the flower
   patch is 4 feet long. She also says it is 4 inches
   long. Which measurement is correct? Explain.

   _____

   _____

   _____

Write About It

4. Eladio says his kitchen counter is 200 centimeters
   long and also 2 meters long. Explain how the same
   object can have two different measurements.

   _____

   _____

   _____

Compare Lengths

How many inches longer is the green pencil than the red pencil?

Objective
- Measure to find how much longer one object is than another.

Math Word
length

You can measure objects to compare lengths.

- First, line up both pencils with the 0 mark of the inch ruler.

  The red pencil is 4 inches long.
  The green pencil is 6 inches long.

- Then count how many inches from the end of the red pencil to the end of the green pencil.

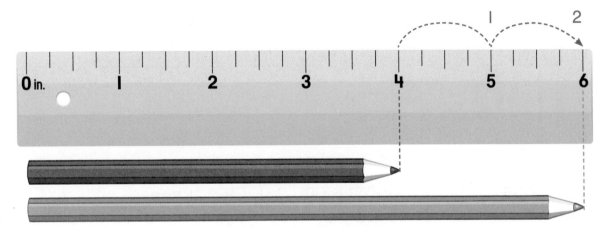

There are 2 inches between the end of the red pencil and the end of the green pencil.

> The green pencil is 2 inches longer than the red pencil. The red pencil is 2 inches shorter than the green pencil.

Use the drawing for Exercises 1–2.

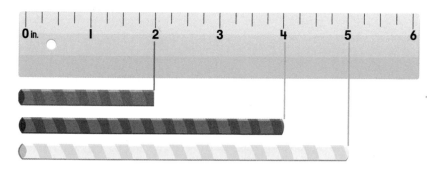

1. The blue straw is ____ in. shorter than the pink straw.

2. The yellow straw is ____ in. longer than the pink straw.

Problem Solving

3. Taylor's bike is 6 feet shorter than her mom's car. How long is Taylor's bike?

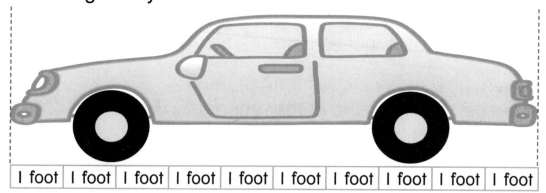

| 1 foot | 1 foot | 1 foot | 1 foot | 1 foot | 1 foot | 1 foot | 1 foot | 1 foot | 1 foot |

Taylor's bike is ____ feet long.

Write About It

4. Evan's rope is shorter than his dad's garden hose. How long could Evan's rope be? How much longer would the hose be?

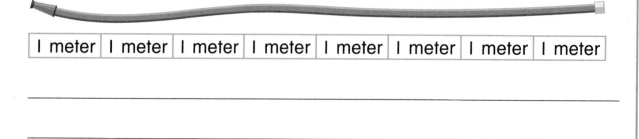

| 1 meter | 1 meter | 1 meter | 1 meter | 1 meter | 1 meter | 1 meter | 1 meter |

_____

_____

Name _____

Add and Subtract Lengths

Objective
■ Use addition and subtraction to solve word problems involving lengths.

Math Word
inch

Marcus measures his toy skateboard.

He uses the length of the toy skateboard to help find the lengths of other toys.

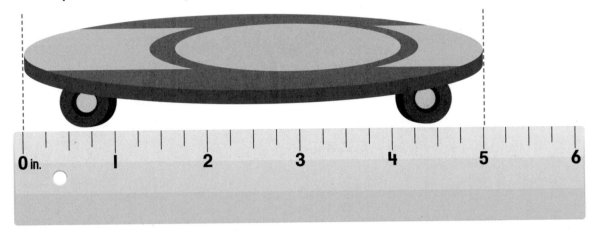

A toy train is 4 inches longer than the toy skateboard. How long is the train?

Add 4 to the length of the toy skateboard.

$$5 + 4 = ?$$

$$5 + 4 = 9$$

➤ The toy train is 9 inches long.

A toy car is 2 inches shorter than the toy skateboard. How long is the car?

Subtract 2 from the length of the toy skateboard.

$$5 - 2 = ?$$

$$5 - 2 = 3$$

➤ The toy car is 3 inches long.

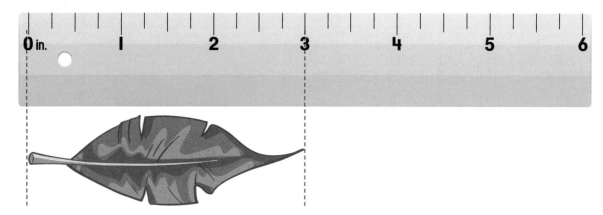

PRACTICE

Use addition to solve the problem.

1. Axel's feather is 4 inches longer than the feather in the drawing. How long is Axel's feather?

   ____ + ____ = ____

   Axel's feather is ____ inches long.

Problem Solving

2. Kwan's picture is 32 cm long.
   Ben's picture is 14 cm shorter
   than Kwan's. How long is Ben's picture?

   Ben's picture is ____ cm long.

Write About It

3. A piece of string is 36 inches long. Another piece is 24 inches long. Rhonda says the total length of the two pieces is 50 inches. Is she correct? Explain.

   _____

   _____

   _____

LESSON 6-9

Name_____

Problem Solving
More Than One Way

Read ⟩ Plan ⟩ Solve ⟩ Check

Austin measures his toothbrush and toothpaste. How many centimeters longer is Austin's toothbrush than his toothpaste?

Choose a strategy to solve the problem.

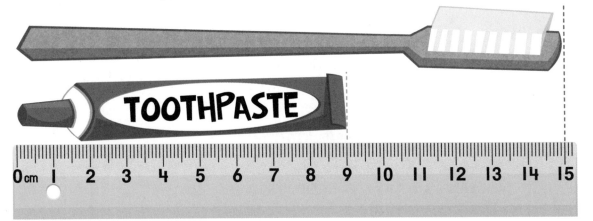

◆ You can write an equation to find the difference.

Write a subtraction equation.	Write an addition equation.
$15 - 9 = ?$	$9 + ? = 15$
$15 - 9 = 6$	$9 + 6 = 15$

◆ You can compare lengths on the ruler.

Count how many centimeters are between the two lengths.

➤ Both strategies give the same answer. The toothbrush is 6 centimeters longer than the toothpaste.

Choose a strategy to solve each problem.

1. How much longer is the tool than the nail? _____ inches

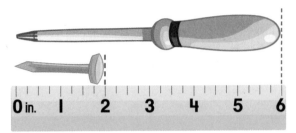

Use the ruler to help you. Count the inches from the end of the nail to the end of the tool.

What strategy did you use?

_____

2. Emma's shoe is 22 centimeters long.
   Lily's shoe is 14 centimeters long.
   How much longer is Emma's shoe than Lily's?

   Emma's shoe is _____ cm longer.

   What strategy did you use?

   _____

   _____

Write About It

3. The length of a box is 24 inches and the height is 18 inches. Ellen says that the height is 16 inches less than the length. Is Ellen correct? Explain.

   _____

   _____

   _____

Problem Solving
More Than One Way

How many centimeters longer is the toothbrush than the toothpaste? Choose a strategy to solve the problem.

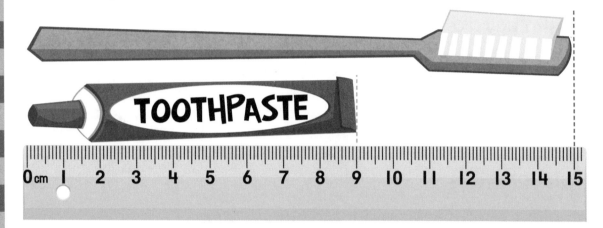

◆ You can write an addition equation or a subtraction equation.

$15 - 9 = ?$ $9 + ? = 15$

$15 - 9 = 6$ $9 + 6 = 15$

◆ You can compare lengths on the ruler. Count how many centimeters are between the two lengths.

The toothbrush is 6 centimeters longer than the toothpaste.

Solve.

1. The yellow slide on a playground is 9 feet long. The green slide is 5 feet longer than the yellow slide. How long is the green slide?

   _____ feet

   What strategy did you use to solve the problem?

   _____

   _____

Fill in the distances. Then choose two strategies to solve the problem.

2. Samuel and Ben measured the distance each threw a paper airplane. Samuel threw his plane

   ____ meters. Ben threw his plane ____ meters. How much farther did Samuel's plane fly? Show two different strategies to solve the problem.

Strategy 1:
Strategy 2:

   Samuel's plane flew ____ meters farther than Ben's plane.

   Which strategy do you think was better to solve this problem? Why?

   _____

   _____

   _____

HOMEWORK

Choose a strategy to solve the problem.

1. How many centimeters longer is the marker than

   the scissors? ____ cm

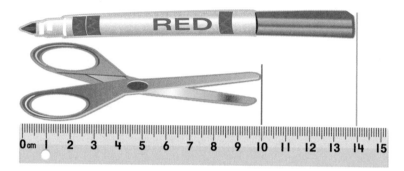

   What strategy did you use?

   _____

   _____

2. Use an inch ruler to measure two objects.
   Record the lengths in inches.

   Object 1: _____   Length: _____ in.

   Object 2: _____   Length: _____ in.

   Compare the lengths of the objects.

   The _____ is _____ inches

   longer than the _____.

   What strategy did you use to solve the problem?
   Why did you use this strategy?

   _____

   _____

Solve.

3. Henry's desk is 1 meter long. His nametag is
8 centimeters long. Henry says his nametag is
7 centimeters longer than his desk. What error
did Henry make? Explain how to correct it.

_____

_____

_____

4. Kayla has 5 rolls of green ribbon. Each roll has
4 meters of green ribbon. She has 6 rolls of blue
ribbon. Each roll has 3 meters of blue ribbon.

Find how many meters Kayla has of each color
ribbon. Explain your strategy. Show your work.

_____

_____

_____

Write About It

5. Which color ribbon does Kayla have more of?
How much more? Explain how you found your answer.

Kayla has _____ meters more of _____ ribbon.

_____

_____

_____

Represent Whole Numbers on a Number Line Diagram

Objective
- Find and represent whole numbers on a number line.

Math Word
number line

Riley found 16 kinds of seeds on a nature hike. Show 16 on a number line.

◆ Count on from 0 to 16. Each tick mark represents one number. The tick mark for 16 has 16 under it.

The numbers become greater as you move to the right.

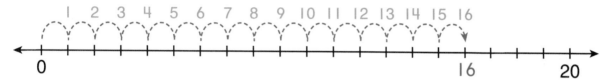

◆ You can also count back from 20 to 16.

The numbers become lesser as you move to the left.

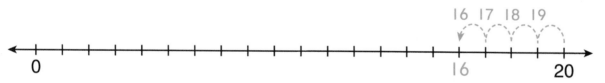

▷ The number 16 is shown on both number lines.

PRACTICE

Find and write the numbers on each number line.

1. 11, 3, and 18

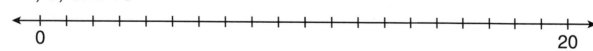

2. 36, 30, and 22

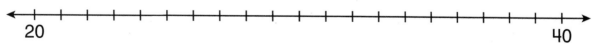

Write the missing number in each box.

3.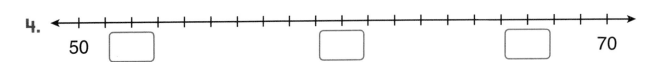

4.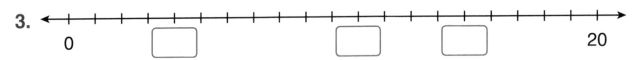

5.

Problem Solving

6. Aiden drew this number line to show the numbers from 0 to 10. Explain what Aiden did wrong.

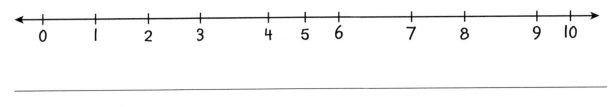

_____

_____

─Write About It⬦─────────────────────────────

7. Look at the number line. Will the number that belongs in the box be greater than or less than 5? Explain how you know.

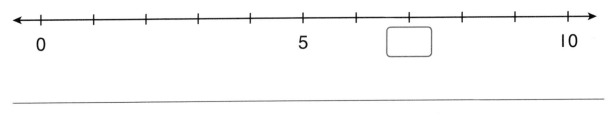

_____

_____

_____

Name_____

Represent Whole Numbers on a Number Line Diagram

Show 16 on a number line.

You can count on from 0 to 16.

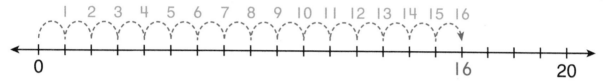

Or, you can count back from 20 to 16.

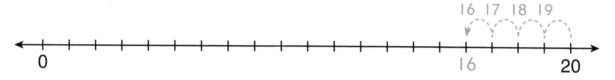

The number 16 is shown on both number lines.

MORE PRACTICE

Find and write the numbers on each number line.

1. 40, 47, and 34

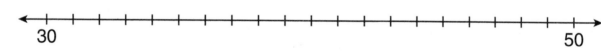

2. 62, 76, and 68

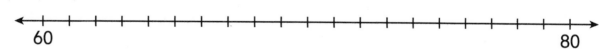

Write the missing number in each box.

3.
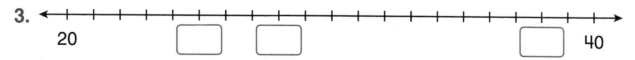

1. Write 49, 41, and 55 on the number line.

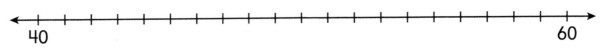

2. Write the missing number in each box.

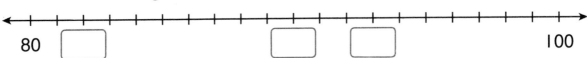

Problem Solving

3. Luis needs to write the number 27 on this number line. Explain two different ways Luis could find where to place 27.

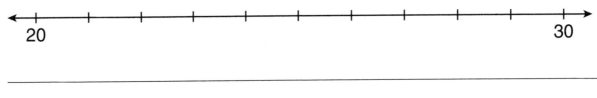

_____

_____

_____

Write About It

4. Look at the number line.

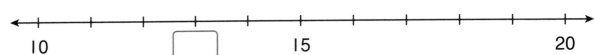

Will the number that belongs in the box be greater than or less than 15? Explain how you know.

_____

_____

_____

Objective
■ Use a number line to add and subtract.

Math Word
number line

Add and Subtract on a Number Line Diagram

Sofia picked 37 carrots. She uses 15 carrots to make soup. How many carrots does Sofia have left?

Use a number line to subtract.

Start at 37 and count back 15.

$15 = 1$ ten 5 ones.

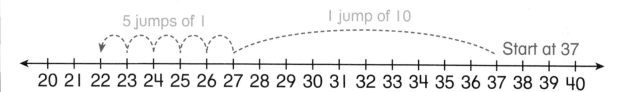

You end on 22.

So, $37 - 15 = 22$.

▷ Sofia has 22 carrots left.

PRACTICE

Use the number line to find the missing number.

1. $36 - $ _____ $= 24$

   Count back 10: $36 - 10 = $ _____

   Count back _____ more.

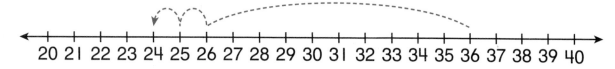

Write the addition or subtraction equation shown.

2. _____ − _____ = _____

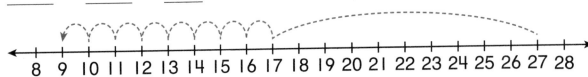

3. _____ + _____ = _____

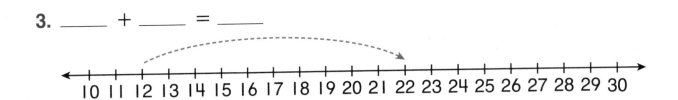

Problem Solving

4. Isaac has 26 coins. Luke has 16 coins. How many coins do they have in all? Use the number line.

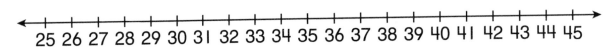

Isaac and Luke have _____ coins in all.

Write About It

5. What math problem does this number line show? Explain how you know.

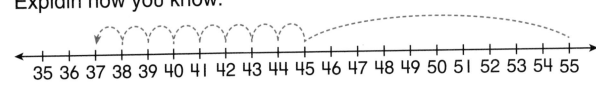

_____

_____

_____

_____

Add and Subtract on a Number Line Diagram

37 − 15 = ?

Use a number line to subtract.

Start at 37 and count back 15.

> You can first count back by 10 and then count back by 1s.

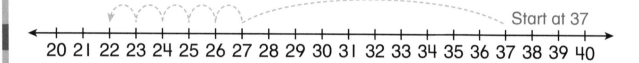

Start at 37

37 − 15 = 22

MORE PRACTICE

Use the number line to find the missing number.

1. 92 − _____ = 79

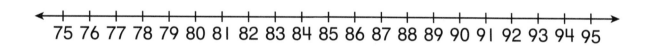

2. 16 + _____ = 24

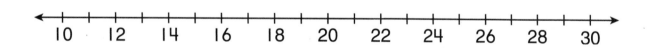

3. 54 + 16 = _____

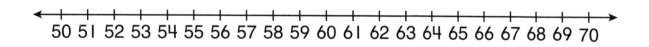

Use the number line to find the missing numbers.

1. _____ + 18 = _____

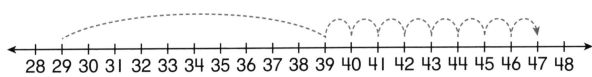

2. 76 − _____ = _____

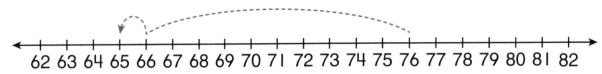

Problem Solving

3. Sierra made 51 bracelets for a craft fair. She sold 17 bracelets. How many bracelets does Sierra have left? Use the number line.

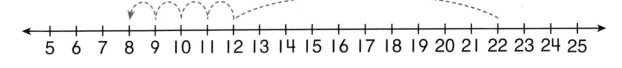

Sierra has _____ bracelets left.

Write About It

4. Kyle says the number line shows 22 − 5 = 8. Explain Kyle's mistake. Then write the correct subtraction problem.

_____

_____

_____

Name_____

Estimate the length in inches. Then use an inch ruler to measure the length.

1.

Estimate: about _____ inches

Measure: about _____ inches

Write the tool and unit you would use to measure the length of the real object. Write *ruler*, *yardstick*, or *measuring tape*. Write *inches*, *feet*, or *yards*.

2.

Tool: _____

Unit: _____

Write the tool and unit you would use to measure the height of the real object. Write *ruler* or *meterstick*. Write *centimeters* or *meters*.

3.

Tool: _____

Unit: _____

Circle the correct words to complete the sentence.

4. It takes fewer (centimeters / meters) to measure a cafeteria table because meters are (smaller / larger) than centimeters.

5. A distance of 12 (feet / inches) is longer than a distance of 12 (feet / inches).

Use the drawing for Exercises 6 and 7.

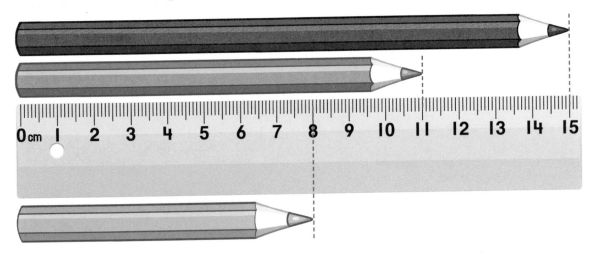

6. The blue pencil is ___ cm longer than the green pencil.

7. The green pencil is ___ cm shorter than the red pencil.

Solve.

8. Hayden is 46 inches tall. Blake is 7 inches taller than Hayden. How tall is Blake?

   Blake is ___ inches tall.

   What strategy did you use to solve the problem?

   _____

   _____

Use the number line to find the sum.

9. $11 + 16 =$ ___

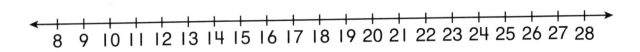

Meteorologists can measure temperature in degrees Celsius (°C). The table shows the daily high temperatures in a town last week.

Monday	Tuesday	Wednesday	Thursday	Friday
20°C	22°C	13°C	12°C	16°C

1. How many degrees warmer was the temperature on Tuesday than on Thursday, in °C?

   It was _____ °C warmer on Tuesday.

2. If Saturday's temperature is 9°C colder than the temperature on Friday, what is the temperature on Saturday? Explain how you found your answer.

   _____

   _____

3. Use the number line to show how much colder the temperature was on Wednesday than on Monday.

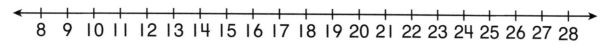

   The temperature on Wednesday was _____ °C colder.

4. Record the daily high temperatures in your town for one school week.

   Write and answer questions comparing the temperatures on specific days.

Name _____

Determine the best answer for each problem.

1. Subtract.

$17 - 8 =$ _____

2. Add.

$6 + 8 =$ _____

3. Add.

$$\begin{array}{r} 5 \\ + \ 7 \\ \hline \end{array}$$

4. Subtract.

$$\begin{array}{r} 1\,8 \\ - \ \ 9 \\ \hline \end{array}$$

5. Write the missing number in the equation.

$16 -$ _____ $= 8$

6. Add.

$7 + 5 + 3 =$ _____

7. How many tens are in 63?

A. 3 tens
B. 6 tens
C. 9 tens

8. Which answer is equal to 28?

A. $2 + 8$
B. $80 + 2$
C. $20 + 8$

9. Ella has 15 fish. 4 are blue, 3 are red, and the rest are pink. How many are pink?

_____ fish are pink.

10. Cody ran 4 miles, 8 miles, and 7 miles last week. How many miles did he run in all?

Cody ran _____ miles in all.

A.M. Letters that show a time at or after midnight and before noon.

---

add To find how many in all.

$$3 + 2 = 5$$

---

addend A number that is added to another number or numbers.

$$\underset{\text{addend}}{6} + \underset{\text{addend}}{4} = 10$$

---

addition equation An addition number sentence with an equal sign.

---

addition fact An equation of the form part + part = whole.

---

angle of a polygon The space between two sides of a polygon that meet.

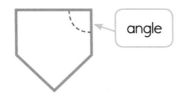

array A set of objects arranged in rows and columns.

Associative Property of Addition Changing the grouping of the addends does not change the sum.
Example:
$$(2 + 6) + 4 = 2 + (6 + 4)$$

bar graph A graph that uses bars to show data. The bars may be of different lengths.

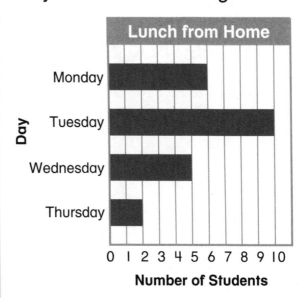

bar model A diagram that uses a series of rectangles to represent the parts and the whole of a problem.

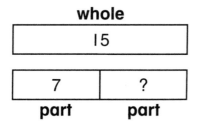

whole

| 15 |

| 7 | ? |
| part | part |

break apart To write a number as the sum of lesser numbers.

45 + 27

40 + 5 + 20 + 7

40 + 20 + 5 + 7

60 + 12

72

centimeter (cm) A unit of metric measure to describe length.

This is 1 centimeter: ⊢—⊣.

centimeter ruler A tool, labeled in centimeters, that is used to measure length.

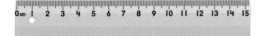

change Money received back when an amount paid is greater than the total amount due.

column A vertical arrangement of objects or numbers.

compare To describe a number as greater than (>), less than (<), or equal to (=) another number.
Example: 153 > 145

cone A solid shape with one curved surface and one flat surface shaped like a circle.

corner The point at which sides of a two-dimensional shape or edges of a three-dimensional shape meet.

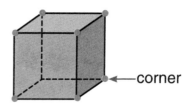

corner

count backwards (count back) To name numbers in decreasing order.

counting on To start at a given number and count forward from that number.

| 5 is greater than 3. Start at 5. | Count on 3. 6, 7, 8 |

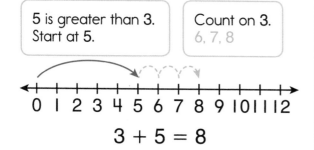

$$3 + 5 = 8$$

cube A solid shape with 6 flat surfaces all shaped like squares.

customary unit A unit in the customary system of measurement.
Examples: inch, foot, and yard

cylinder A solid shape with one curved surface and two flat surfaces shaped like circles.

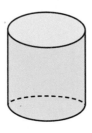

data A set of collected values or information.

diagonal In a table or array, from the bottom left to the top right or from the top left to the bottom right.

diagram A visual model of a problem or solution.

difference The result of subtracting.

digit 0, 1, 2, 3, 4, 5, 6, 7, 8, or 9.

dime A coin that is worth 10 cents.

dollar sign The symbol $.

doubles – I strategy To find a sum where one addend is I more than the other addend, use the doubles fact for the greater addend and subtract I.

Example: since $4 + 4 = 8$
then $4 + 3 = 7$

doubles + I strategy To find a sum where one addend is I more than the other addend, use the doubles fact for the lesser addend and add I.

Example: since $7 + 7 = 14$
then $7 + 8 = 15$

doubles fact A two-addend addition equation in which both addends are the same.

Example: $9 + 9 = 18$

edge The line segment where two faces of a three-dimensional figure meet.

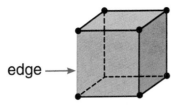

edge →

equal addends Addends that are the same; the sum of two equal addends is always an even number.

equal amounts of money Groups of money that total the same amount even if they are made up of different coins and bills.

equal shares Pieces of one whole that are the same size.

Example: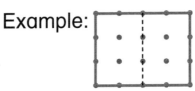

equal sign The symbol =.

equal to (=) To have the same value as.

equals = A symbol that means to have the same value as.

Example: $35 = 35$

equation A number sentence with an equal sign (=) that shows the value on the left side is the same as the value on the right side.

Example: $15 + 10 = 25$

estimate An approximate answer; to find an answer that is close to the exact answer.

even number A number with none left over if you count by 2s or make pairs. Even numbers have 0, 2, 4, 6, or 8 in the ones place.

expanded form A form that shows a number written as the sum of the place values of each digit.

Example: The expanded form of 173 is 100 + 70 + 3.

face A flat surface with straight sides on a three-dimensional figure.

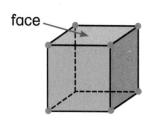

face

fact family A set of related facts for a given group of numbers.

Example: $4 + 7 = 11$
$11 - 7 = 4$
$7 + 4 = 11$
$11 - 4 = 7$

fifty-dollar bill A piece of paper money worth fifty dollars, or $50.

five-dollar bill A piece of paper money worth five dollars, or $5.

foot (ft) A customary unit of measure to describe length that equals 12 inches.

four fourths All parts of a whole that is divided into 4 equal parts.

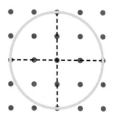

fourth One part of a whole that is divided into 4 equal parts.

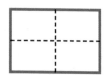

Each equal share is one fourth.

greater than (>) A symbol showing that one number has a greater value than another number.
Example: 27 > 19

greatest Having the largest value.

group To put together.

half One part of a whole that is divided into 2 equal parts.

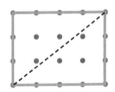

Each equal share is one half.

half hour A measure of time equal to 30 minutes.

half past Describes one half hour or 30 minutes past an hour.

hexagon A flat shape with 6 sides and 6 corners.

hour A unit of time that equals 60 minutes.

hour hand The short hand on an analog clock that shows the hour.

hundred 1 hundred = 10 tens = 100 ones.

hundred flat A square divided into 100 equal parts.

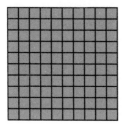

inch (in.) A customary unit of measure to describe length. This is 1 inch: .

inch ruler A tool used to measure length in inches.

key A statement showing how many data items each symbol stands for in a picture graph.

Favorite Type of Book	
Fiction	📘📘📘📘📘📘📘📘
Nonfiction	📘📘📘📘
Key: Each 📘 stands for 1 friend.	

The key tells how many each symbol stands for.

L

least Having the smallest value.

length Measurement along a straight line from end to end.

less than (<) A symbol showing that one number has a lesser value than another number.
Example: 32 < 47

line plot A graph that uses X marks on a number line to represent data.

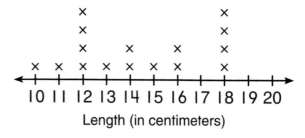
Pencil Lengths

logical reasoning Using correct thought processes and steps to solve a problem.

make 10   A strategy for adding or subtracting in which numbers in the problem are broken apart to form sums or differences equal to 10.

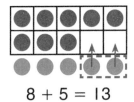

8 + 5 = 13

measure   To describe an object with a number by using a tool such as a ruler.

measuring tape   A long, flexible strip of plastic or metal that is marked at intervals for measuring length.

meter (m)   A metric unit of measure that is equal to 100 centimeters.

meterstick   A ruler used to measure length in centimeters and meters.

metric unit   A unit in the metric system of measurement. Examples: centimeters and meters

minus sign (−)   A symbol that means to subtract or take away.

minute   A unit of time that equals 60 seconds.

minute hand   The long hand on an analog clock that shows the minute.

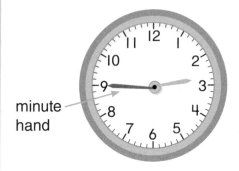

minute hand

model   A diagram or picture that represents a problem or helps to solve a problem.

6   +   4   =   10

N

near doubles fact   A two-addend addition equation in which one addend is 1 more or 1 less than the other.

nickel A coin worth 5 cents.

number line A line that shows numbers in order using a scale.

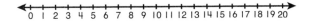

number name The word form for a number.
Example: 96 is ninety-six

odd number A number with one left over if you count by 2s or make pairs. Odd numbers have 1, 3, 5, 7, or 9 in the ones place.

one-dollar bill A piece of paper money worth one dollar, or $1.

one hundred-dollar bill A piece of paper money worth one hundred dollars, or $100.

one less A number less than another number by 1.

one more A number greater than another number by 1.

ones 10 ones = 1 ten

P.M. Letters that show a time at or after noon and before midnight.

pattern An arrangement of objects or values that follows a rule.

pattern rule A rule that tells what order objects appear in a pattern.

penny A coin worth 1 cent.

pentagon A polygon with 5 sides and 5 angles.

picture graph A graph that uses pictures to represent numbers of real-world objects.

Favorite Season	
Fall	🍁 🍁 🍁 🍁
Winter	🍁 🍁 🍁 🍁 🍁
Spring	🍁 🍁 🍁
Summer	🍁 🍁 🍁 🍁 🍁 🍁 🍁
Key: Each 🍁 stands for 1 student.	

place value The value of a digit depending on its position, or place, in a number.

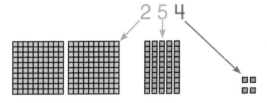

2 5 4

The 2 is in the hundreds place.

Its value is 200.

The 5 is in the tens place.

Its value is 50.

The 4 is in the ones place.

Its value is 4.

place-value chart A chart that shows the value of each digit in a number.

hundreds	tens	ones
2	5	4

plus sign (+) A symbol that means to add.

polygon A closed plane figure made up of line segments that meet at vertices but do not cross.

pyramid A solid figure whose base is a polygon and whose faces are triangles with a common vertex.

Q

quadrilateral A polygon with 4 sides and 4 angles.

Examples: rectangle, square, trapezoid

quarter A coin worth 25 cents.

R

rectangle A shape with 4 sides and 4 corners.

rectangular prism A solid figure with 6 rectangular faces.

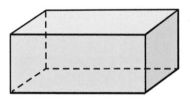

regroup To rename ten in a place as one in the next greater place, or one in a place as ten in the next lesser place, in order to add or subtract.

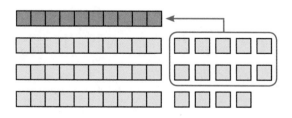

related addition facts Addition facts that use the same numbers.

$$3 + 8 = 11$$
$$8 + 3 = 11$$

related subtraction facts Subtraction facts that use the same numbers.

$$12 - 3 = 9$$
$$12 - 9 = 3$$

row A horizontal arrangement of objects or numbers.

ruler A tool used to measure length, usually labeled in inches along one edge and centimeters on the opposite edge.

S

side A line segment that forms part of a shape.

skip count To count by a number that is not 1. Example: Skip count from 0 by 2s: 2, 4, 6, 8, 10

sphere A round three-dimensional figure.

square A shape with 4 sides of equal length and 4 corners.

standard form of a number The numeral form of a number.

subtract To take away; to find how many are left.

$6 - 2 = 4$

subtraction equation A subtraction number sentence with an equal sign. Example: $9 - 6 = 3$

sum The result of adding.

$$6 \quad + \quad 4 \quad = \quad 10$$

sum

symbol A picture or character that stands for something. Key: Each stands for I student.   symbol

T

table An organized chart of rows and columns.

Fruit	Number Sold
Peaches	133
Apples	167
Bananas	138
Mangoes	159

take apart To separate a group into two or more smaller groups.

$10 - 3 = 7$

tally chart A chart that organizes data and uses tally marks to record frequency.

Jump Distances	
Distance (in feet)	Tally
3	II
4	⯑ II
5	⯑
6	I

tally mark A mark used in a tally chart to help record frequency of data.

ten-dollar bill A piece of paper money worth ten dollars, or $10.

ten-frame A rectangular chart with 2 rows and 5 columns that is used to represent numbers less than or equal to 10.

tens number A number with tens and no ones.

third One part of a whole that is divided into 3 equal parts.

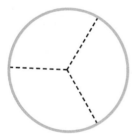

Each equal share is one third.

three thirds All parts of a whole that is divided into 3 equal parts.

three-digit number A number consisting of hundreds, tens, and ones.

hundreds	tens	ones
5	6	4

five hundred sixty-four 564

three-dimensional shape A solid figure that has measurements of length, width, and height.

triangle A shape with 3 sides and 3 corners.

twenty-dollar bill A piece of paper money worth twenty dollars, or $20.

two-dimensional shape A shape with length and width, but no thickness.

two halves All parts of a whole that is divided into 2 equal parts.

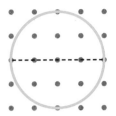

unknown A missing value or part.

unknown addend An addend whose value is not known and is usually represented by a box or a question mark.

vertex (vertices) The point where three edges of a solid figure meet.

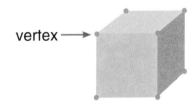

vertex ⟶

whole All of something.

whole number Any of the numbers 0, 1, 2, 3, 4, ...

work backward A strategy where the answer is known and the unknown is found by reversing the operations or steps in the problem.

Y

yard (yd) A customary unit of measure to describe length that equals 3 feet.

yardstick A ruler used to measure length in feet and yards.

tens	ones

tens	ones

tens	ones

tens	ones

tens	ones

tens	ones

tens	ones

tens	ones

tens	ones

tens	ones

tens	ones

tens	ones

tens	ones

tens	ones

tens	ones

dimes	pennies

dimes	pennies

h	t	o

h	t	o

dimes	pennies

dimes	pennies

h	t	o

h	t	o

Addition and Subtraction Frames

1	2	3	4	5	6	7	8	9	10
11	12	13	14	15	16	17	18	19	20
21	22	23	24	25	26	27	28	29	30
31	32	33	34	35	36	37	38	39	40
41	42	43	44	45	46	47	48	49	50
51	52	53	54	55	56	57	58	59	60
61	62	63	64	65	66	67	68	69	70
71	72	73	74	75	76	77	78	79	80
81	82	83	84	85	86	87	88	89	90
91	92	93	94	95	96	97	98	99	100

Hundred Chart

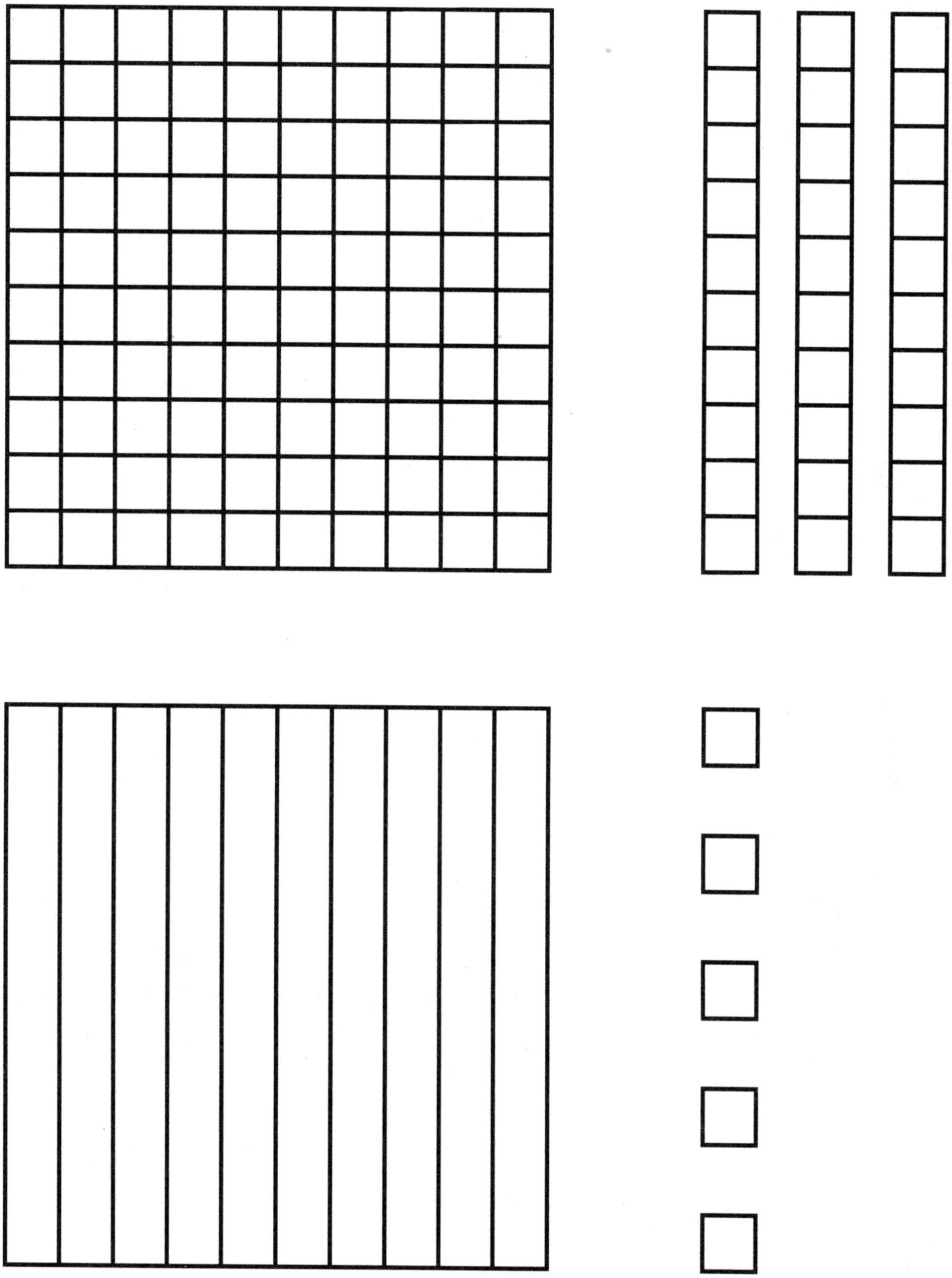

Base Ten Blocks

hundreds	tens	ones	Write the number.

Place-Value Workmat

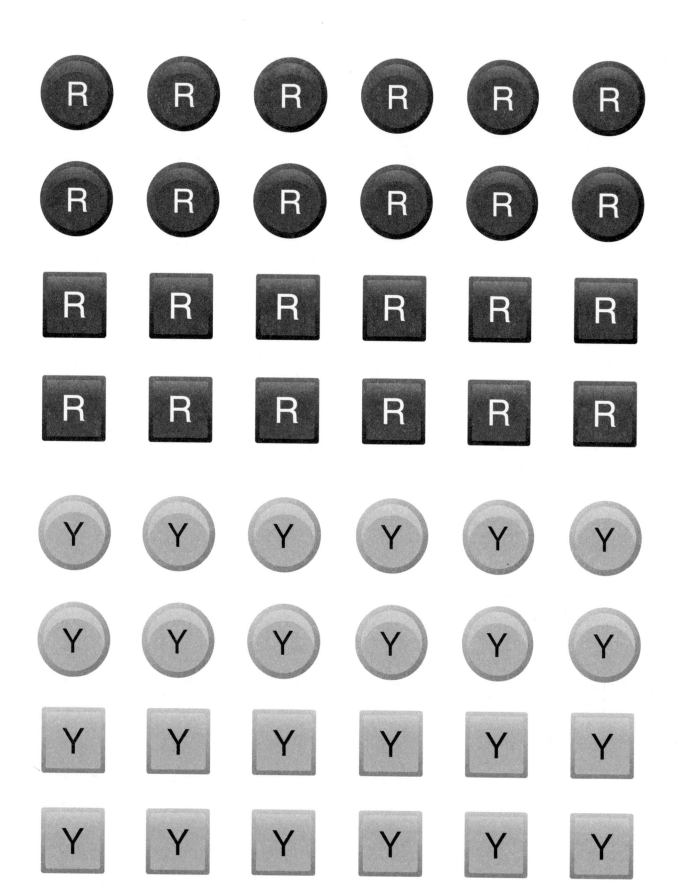

Counters

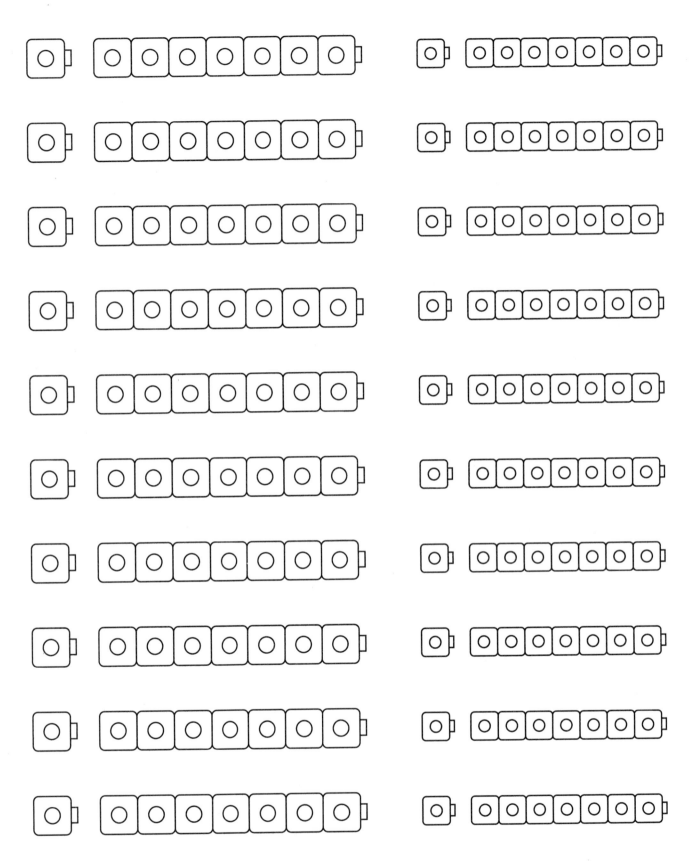

Connecting Cubes

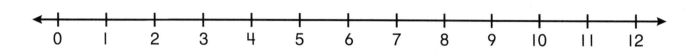

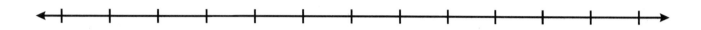

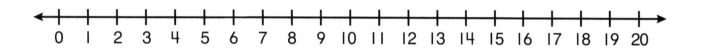

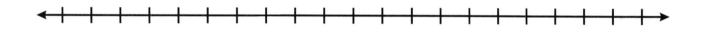

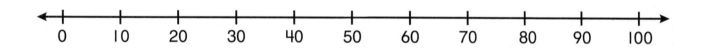

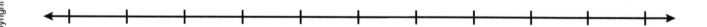

Number Lines

Number Bonds

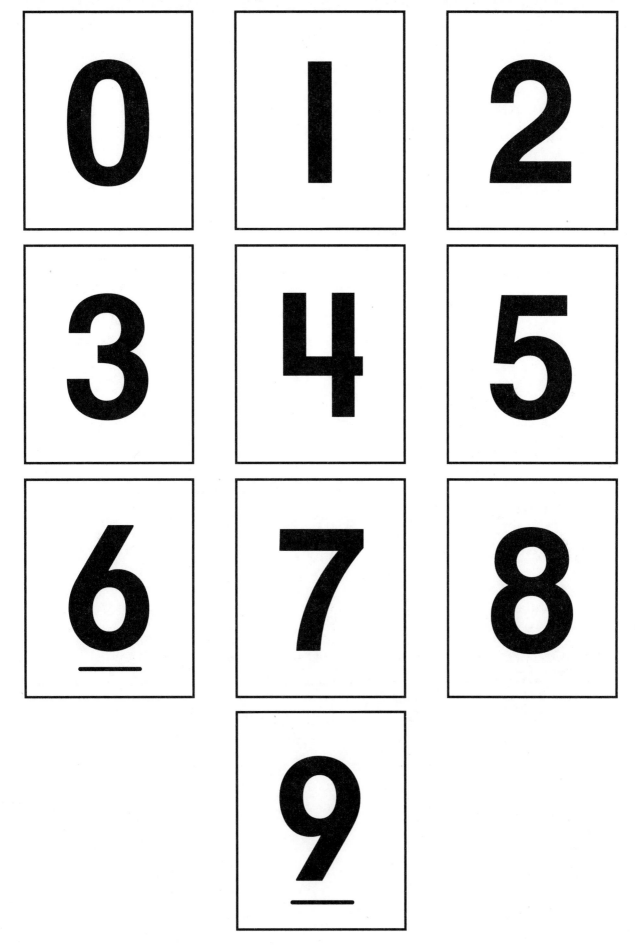

Number Tiles

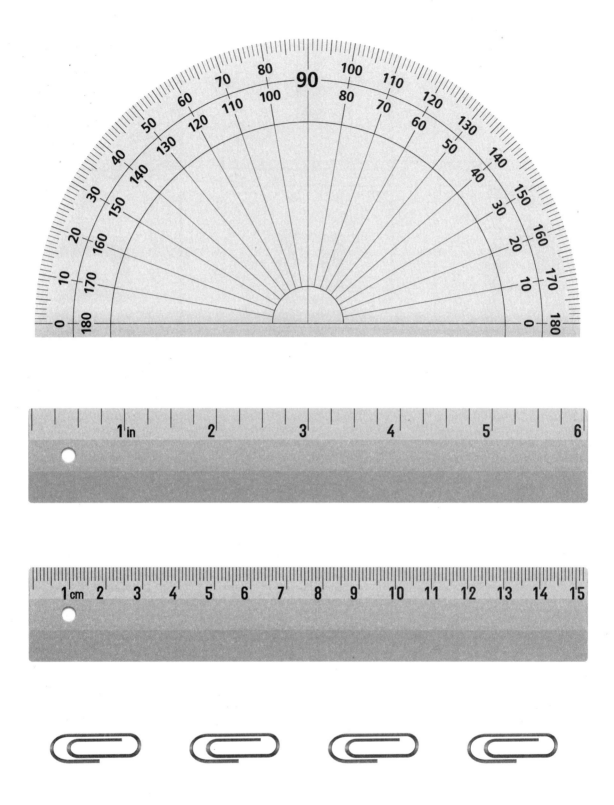

Measurement